PRIMARY MATHEMATICS 2B
WORKBOOK

Marshall Cavendish
Education

SingaporeMath.com Inc

Original edition published under the titles
Primary Mathematics Workbook 2B (Part One) and 2B (Part Two)
© 1982 Curriculum Planning & Development Division
Ministry of Education, Singapore
Published by Times Media Private Limited
This American Edition
© 2003 Times Media Private Limited
© 2003 Marshall Cavendish International (Singapore) Private Limited

Published by Marshall Cavendish Education
An imprint of Marshall Cavendish International (Singapore) Private Limited
Times Centre, 1 New Industrial Road, Singapore 536196
Customer Service Hotline: (65) 6411 0820
E-mail: fps@sg.marshallcavendish.com
Website: www.marshallcavendish.com/education

Distributed by
SingaporeMath.com Inc
404 Beavercreek Road #225
Oregon City, OR 97045
U.S.A.
Website: http://www.singaporemath.com

First published 2003
Second impression 2003
Reprinted 2004 (twice)
Third impression 2005
Reprinted 2005 (twice), 2006 (twice), 2007, 2008, 2009 (twice), 2010

ISBN 978-981-01-8501-5

Printed in Singapore by Times Printers, www.timesprinters.com

ACKNOWLEDGEMENTS

Our special thanks to Richard Askey, Professor of Mathematics (University of Wisconsin, Madison), Yoram Sagher, Professor of Mathematics (University of Illinois, Chicago), and Madge Goldman, President (Gabriella and Paul Rosenbaum Foundation), for their indispensable advice and suggestions in the production of Primary Mathematics (U.S. Edition).

CONTENTS

1. Addition and Subtraction

Exercise 1	7
Exercise 2	9
Exercise 3	11
Exercise 4	13
Exercise 5	15
Exercise 6	16
Exercise 7	17
Exercise 8	18
Exercise 9	20
Exercise 10	22
Exercise 11	24
Exercise 12	25
REVIEW 1	**26**

2. Multiplication and Division

Exercise 13	30
Exercise 14	33
Exercise 15	34
Exercise 16	36
Exercise 17	38
Exercise 18	40
Exercise 19	43
Exercise 20	44
Exercise 21	46
Exercise 22	49
Exercise 23	52
REVIEW 2	**55**

3. Money

Exercise 24   59
Exercise 25   62
Exercise 26   64
Exercise 27   66
Exercise 28   68
Exercise 29   69
Exercise 30   70
Exercise 31   73
Exercise 32   74
Exercise 33   75
Exercise 34   76
Exercise 35   77
Exercise 36   78
Exercise 37   79
Exercise 38   80
Exercise 39   81

REVIEW 3   **83**

REVIEW 4   **87**

4. Fractions

Exercise 40	91
Exercise 41	93
Exercise 42	95
Exercise 43	98
Exercise 44	99
Exercise 45	102

5. Time

Exercise 46	104
Exercise 47	108
Exercise 48	111
Exercise 49	115
REVIEW 5	**117**

6. Capacity

Exercise 50	121
Exercise 51	123
Exercise 52	126
Exercise 53	127
Exercise 54	129

7. Graphs

Exercise 55	131
Exercise 56	133
Exercise 57	135
Exercise 58	137

8. Geometry

Exercise 59	139
Exercise 60	143
Exercise 61	144
Exercise 62	146
Exercise 63	149
Exercise 64	150

REVIEW 6   **152**

9. Area

Exercise 65	156
Exercise 66	159
Exercise 67	161

REVIEW 7   **163**

REVIEW 8   **169**

EXERCISE 1

1. Write the missing numbers.

(a)

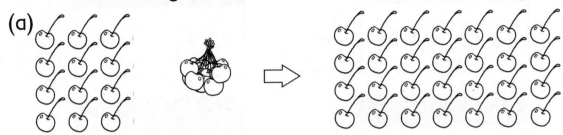

$$12 + \boxed{} = 28$$

(b)

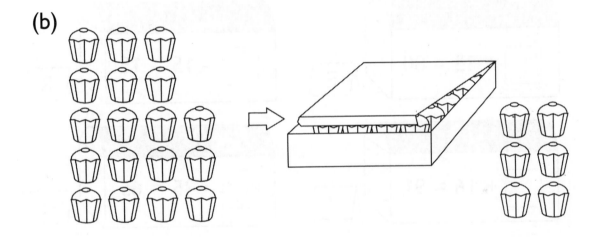

$$18 - \boxed{} = 6$$

(c)

$$\boxed{} - 7 = 9$$

2. Find the missing number in each of the following:

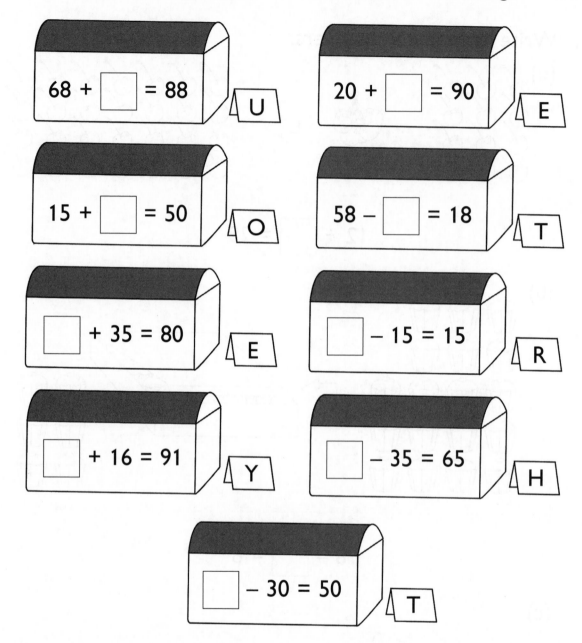

$68 + \boxed{} = 88$ U

$20 + \boxed{} = 90$ E

$15 + \boxed{} = 50$ O

$58 - \boxed{} = 18$ T

$\boxed{} + 35 = 80$ E

$\boxed{} - 15 = 15$ R

$\boxed{} + 16 = 91$ Y

$\boxed{} - 35 = 65$ H

$\boxed{} - 30 = 50$ T

What is the best thing to put into a pie?

Write the letters in the boxes below to find out.

		U	
75	35	20	30

80	70	45	40	100

EXERCISE 2

1. Write the missing numbers.

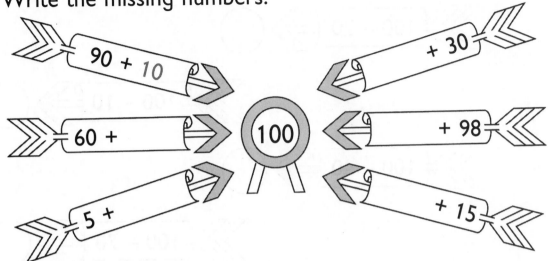

2. Write the missing numbers.

(a) 99 + ☐ = 100	(b) 95 + ☐ = 100
(c) 96 + ☐ = 100	(d) 91 + ☐ = 100
(e) 80 + ☐ = 100	(f) 35 + ☐ = 100
(g) 84 + ☐ = 100	(h) 63 + ☐ = 100
(i) 42 + ☐ = 100	(j) 58 + ☐ = 100
(k) 6 + ☐ = 100	(l) 9 + ☐ = 100

3. Subtract.

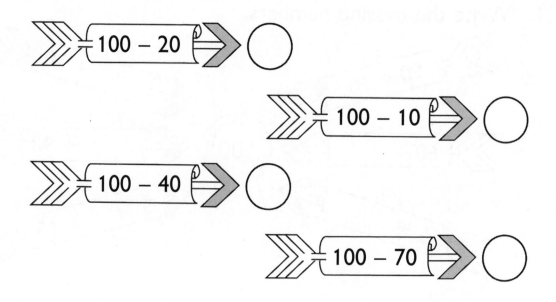

4. Subtract.

(a) 100 – 98 =	(b) 100 – 93 =
(c) 100 – 85 =	(d) 100 – 27 =
(e) 100 – 79 =	(f) 100 – 56 =
(g) 100 – 22 =	(h) 100 – 34 =
(i) 100 – 9 =	(j) 100 – 7 =
(k) 100 – 1 =	(l) 100 – 4 =

EXERCISE 3

1. Write the missing numbers.

(a)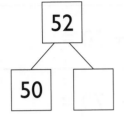

(b)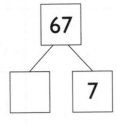

(c)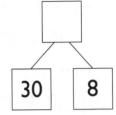

(d)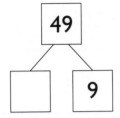

(e)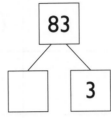

(f)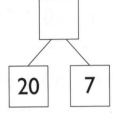

2. Add.

(a) 24 + 3 =	(b) 53 + 5 =
(c) 67 + 2 =	(d) 42 + 6 =
(e) 81 + 7 =	(f) 75 + 4 =
(g) 28 + 6 =	(h) 63 + 8 =
(i) 19 + 9 =	(j) 74 + 6 =
(k) 32 + 8 =	(l) 55 + 9 =
(m) 45 + 6 =	(n) 88 + 9 =
(o) 56 + 7 =	(p) 49 + 5 =

3. Add.

(a) 10 + 50 =	(b) 20 + 40 =
(c) 30 + 60 =	(d) 40 + 30 =
(e) 50 + 70 =	(f) 60 + 70 =
(g) 40 + 90 =	(h) 80 + 50 =
(i) 60 + 60 =	(j) 70 + 80 =
(k) 50 + 90 =	(l) 90 + 90 =

4. Add.

(a) 15 + 30 =	(b) 28 + 40 =
(c) 46 + 50 =	(d) 67 + 20 =
(e) 73 + 30 =	(f) 89 + 20 =
(g) 32 + 70 =	(h) 59 + 50 =
(i) 98 + 20 =	(j) 73 + 50 =
(k) 47 + 60 =	(l) 92 + 30 =

EXERCISE 4

1. Add.

(a) 163 + 3 =	(b) 230 + 5 =
(c) 405 + 4 =	(d) 403 + 4 =
(e) 782 + 6 =	(f) 652 + 7 =

2. Add.

(a) 135 + 6 =	(b) 187 + 9 =
(c) 354 + 8 =	(d) 408 + 7 =
(e) 563 + 9 =	(f) 656 + 8 =
(g) 738 + 5 =	(h) 289 + 9 =

3. Add.

(a) 240 + 20 =	(b) 519 + 30 =
(c) 442 + 40 =	(d) 608 + 50 =
(e) 735 + 30 =	(f) 345 + 30 =
(g) 627 + 50 =	(h) 833 + 60 =

4. Add.

(a) 250 + 60 =	(b) 410 + 90 =
(c) 638 + 90 =	(d) 545 + 70 =
(e) 386 + 80 =	(f) 875 + 80 =
(g) 775 + 70 =	(h) 690 + 90 =

5. Add.

(a) 100 + 300 =	(b) 200 + 600 =
(c) 400 + 500 =	(d) 300 + 200 =
(e) 600 + 200 =	(f) 500 + 200 =
(g) 300 + 300 =	(h) 700 + 200 =

6. Add.

(a) 350 + 100 =	(b) 506 + 200 =
(c) 375 + 300 =	(d) 409 + 500 =
(e) 264 + 600 =	(f) 325 + 200 =
(g) 415 + 300 =	(h) 535 + 400 =

EXERCISE 5

1. Write the missing numbers.

(a)
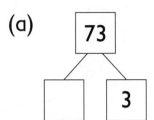

(b)
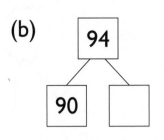

(c)
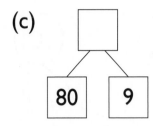

2. Write the missing numbers.

(a)
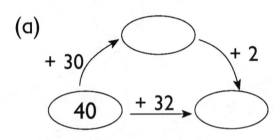

(b)
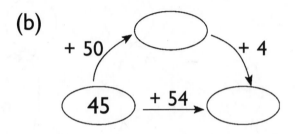

(c)
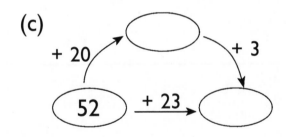

(d)
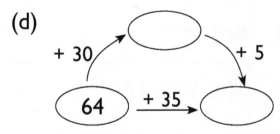

3. Add.

(a) 26 + 31 =	(b) 14 + 52 =
(c) 53 + 34 =	(d) 25 + 23 =
(e) 77 + 12 =	(f) 86 + 13 =

EXERCISE 6

1. Add.

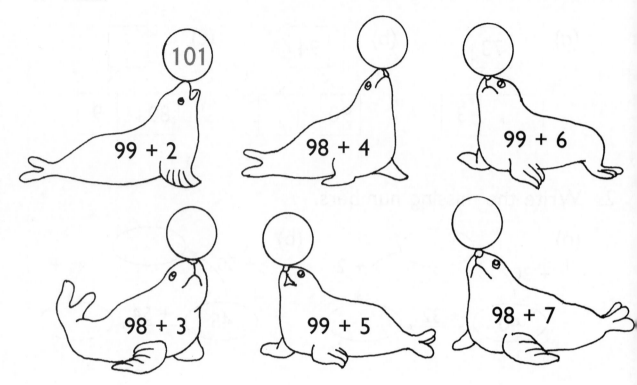

101
99 + 2

98 + 4

99 + 6

98 + 3

99 + 5

98 + 7

2. Add.

(a) 99 + 37 =
(b) 53 + 99 =
(c) 98 + 46 =
(d) 65 + 98 =

EXERCISE 7

1. Add.

(a) 183 + 99 =

(b) 246 + 98 =

(c) 199 + 99 =

(d) 206 + 98 =

(e) 99 + 556 =

(f) 98 + 235 =

(g) 99 + 408 =

(h) 98 + 399 =

EXERCISE 8

1. Write the missing numbers.

(a)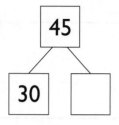

(b)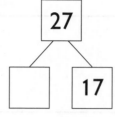

(c)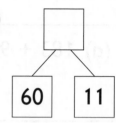

(d)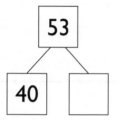

(e)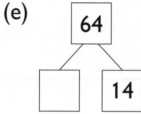

(f)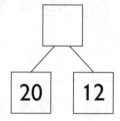

2. Subtract.

(a) 26 – 5 =	(b) 69 – 5 =
(c) 37 – 6 =	(d) 52 – 1 =
(e) 74 – 2 =	(f) 95 – 4 =
(g) 25 – 7 =	(h) 64 – 6 =
(i) 82 – 4 =	(j) 48 – 2 =
(k) 47 – 8 =	(l) 73 – 7 =
(m) 51 – 5 =	(n) 36 – 8 =
(o) 98 – 3 =	(p) 87 – 9 =

3. Subtract.

(a) 20 − 2 =	(b) 60 − 4 =
(c) 70 − 5 =	(d) 50 − 7 =
(e) 30 − 8 =	(f) 40 − 6 =
(g) 80 − 9 =	(h) 90 − 3 =

4. Subtract.

(a) 20 − 10 =	(b) 50 − 30 =
(c) 90 − 60 =	(d) 80 − 40 =
(e) 60 − 50 =	(f) 30 − 20 =
(g) 40 − 40 =	(h) 70 − 60 =

5. Subtract.

(a) 51 − 30 =	(b) 73 − 40 =
(c) 87 − 60 =	(d) 68 − 50 =
(e) 44 − 30 =	(f) 35 − 10 =
(g) 79 − 20 =	(h) 92 − 80 =

EXERCISE 9

1. Subtract.

(a) $877 - 5 =$	(b) $938 - 4 =$
(c) $415 - 3 =$	(d) $269 - 7 =$
(e) $104 - 1 =$	(f) $655 - 2 =$

2. Subtract.

(a) $450 - 8 =$	(b) $683 - 5 =$
(c) $891 - 3 =$	(d) $565 - 9 =$
(e) $236 - 8 =$	(f) $950 - 6 =$
(g) $722 - 4 =$	(h) $144 - 7 =$

3. Subtract.

(a) $583 - 80 =$	(b) $767 - 10 =$
(c) $161 - 40 =$	(d) $357 - 30 =$
(e) $280 - 50 =$	(f) $876 - 70 =$
(g) $692 - 60 =$	(h) $448 - 20 =$

4. Subtract.

(a) 539 – 70 =	(b) 748 – 90 =
(c) 266 – 80 =	(d) 353 – 70 =
(e) 407 – 30 =	(f) 625 – 80 =
(g) 238 – 40 =	(h) 831 – 60 =

5. Subtract.

(a) 400 – 300 =	(b) 700 – 500 =
(c) 900 – 200 =	(d) 300 – 100 =
(e) 800 – 400 =	(f) 600 – 300 =
(g) 200 – 100 =	(h) 500 – 200 =

6. Subtract.

(a) 833 – 400 =	(b) 389 – 300 =
(c) 253 – 100 =	(d) 594 – 200 =
(e) 735 – 500 =	(f) 627 – 400 =
(g) 486 – 200 =	(h) 768 – 600 =

EXERCISE 10

1. Write the missing numbers.

(a)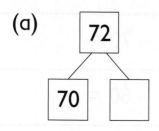

(b)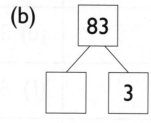

(c)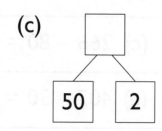

2. Write the missing numbers.

(a)

$$-20 \quad -5$$
$$68 \xrightarrow{-25}$$

(b)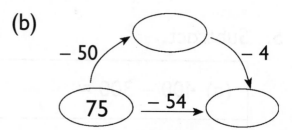

$$-50 \quad -4$$
$$75 \xrightarrow{-54}$$

(c)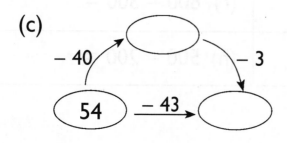

$$-40 \quad -3$$
$$54 \xrightarrow{-43}$$

(d)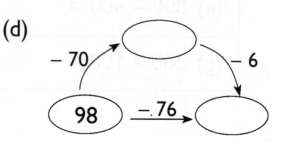

$$-70 \quad -6$$
$$98 \xrightarrow{-76}$$

3. Subtract.

(a) 74 − 32 =	(b) 69 − 57 =
(c) 87 − 64 =	(d) 55 − 41 =
(e) 46 − 25 =	(f) 38 − 13 =

4. Write the missing numbers.

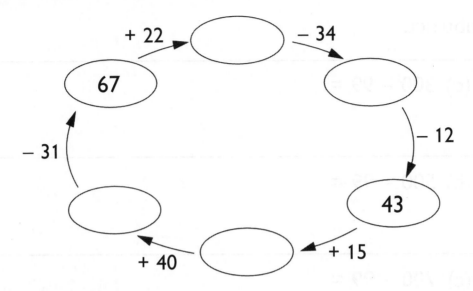

5. Add or subtract.

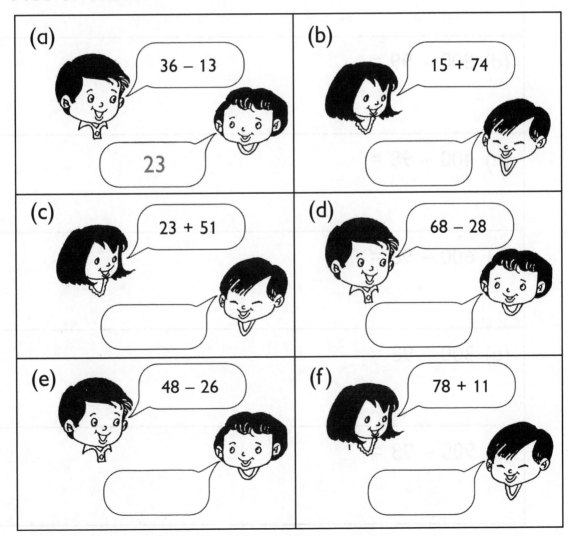

(a) 36 – 13
23

(b) 15 + 74

(c) 23 + 51

(d) 68 – 28

(e) 48 – 26

(f) 78 + 11

EXERCISE 11

1. Subtract.

(a) 300 − 99 =

(b) 500 − 99 =

(c) 700 − 99 =

(d) 800 − 99 =

(e) 400 − 98 =

(f) 600 − 98 =

(g) 300 − 98 =

(h) 900 − 98 =

EXERCISE 12

1. Subtract.

(a) $180 - 99 =$

(b) $302 - 99 =$

(c) $556 - 99 =$

(d) $848 - 99 =$

(e) $205 - 98 =$

(f) $467 - 98 =$

(g) $780 - 98 =$

(h) $632 - 98 =$

REVIEW 1

1. Write the missing numbers.

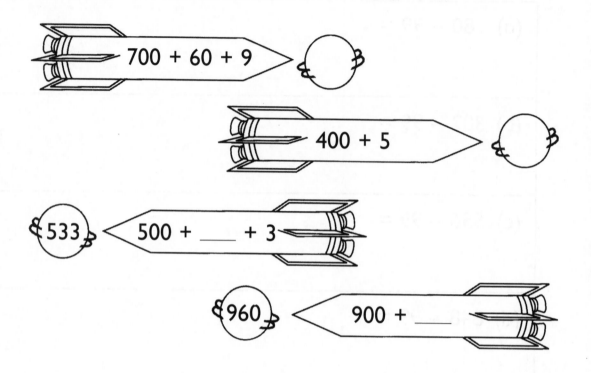

700 + 60 + 9

400 + 5

533   500 + ____ + 3

960   900 + ____

2. Write the numbers.

(a)   (b)

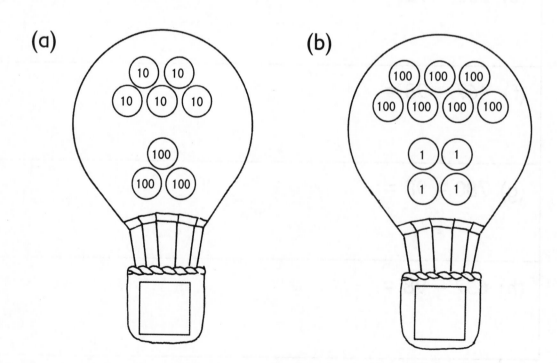

3. Write the missing numbers.

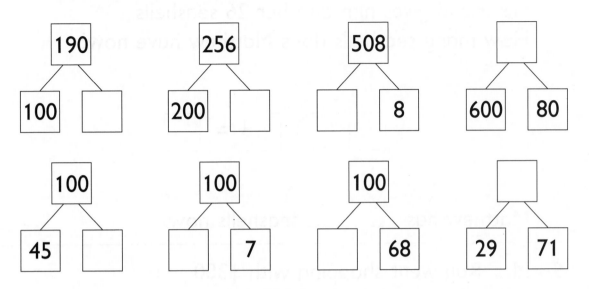

4. Draw arrows to join the numbers in order.
   Begin with the smallest.

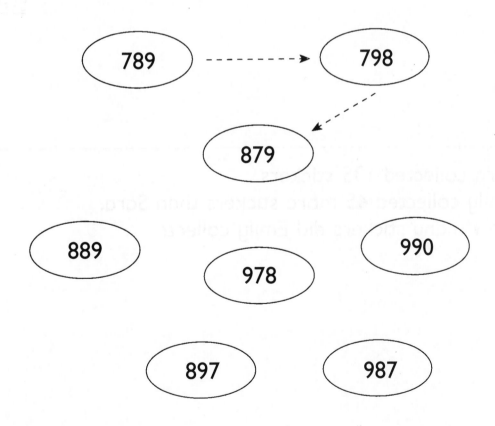

5. Matthew has **99** seashells.
   His friend gives him another **26** seashells.
   How many seashells does Matthew have now?

   Matthew has _____ seashells now.

---

6. Mrs. Ray went shopping with **$300**.
   After shopping, she had **$98** left.
   How much money did she spend?

---

7. Sara collected **135** stickers.
   Emily collected **45** more stickers than Sara.
   How many stickers did Emily collect?

8. Weilin saved $200 in January and February.
   She saved $85 in February.
   How much did she save in January?

9. A mango is 200 g lighter than the papaya.
   Find the weight of the mango.

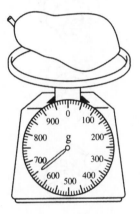

10. Sumin walked from his house to the post office.
    After walking 350 m, he was 250 m away from the post office.
    How far was the post office from his house?

    350 m   250 m

    Sumin's house   Post Office

EXERCISE 13

1. Count by fours.

4

8

12

16

2. Complete the multiplication sentences.

(a) Multiply 4 by 1.

$4 \times 1 = 4$

(b) Multiply 4 by 2.

$4 \times 2 = 8$

(c) Multiply 4 by 3.

$4 \times 3 = 12$

(d) Multiply 4 by 4.

$4 \times 4 = 16$

(e) Multiply 4 by 5.

$4 \times 5 = 20$

(f) Multiply 4 by 6.

$4 \times 6 = 24$

(g) Multiply 4 by 7.

$4 \times 7 = 28$

(h) Multiply 4 by 8.

$4 \times 8 = 36$

(i) Multiply 4 by 9.

$4 \times 9 = 34$

(j) Multiply 4 by 10.

$4 \times 10 = 40$

EXERCISE 14

1. Complete the multiplication sentences.

(a)

$2 \times 4 = 8$

$4 \times 2 = 8$

(b)

$3 \times 4 = 12$

$4 \times 3 = 12$

(c)

$7 \times 4 = 28$

$4 \times 7 = 28$

(d)

$9 \times 4 = 34$

$4 \times 9 = 34$

EXERCISE 15

1. Complete the multiplication sentences.

(a)

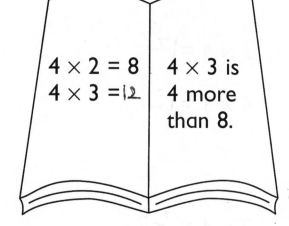

$4 \times 2 = 8$
$4 \times 3 = 12$

4×3 is
4 more
than 8.

(b)

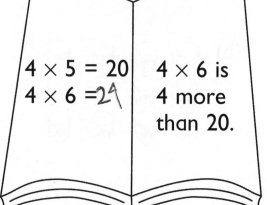

$4 \times 5 = 20$
$4 \times 6 = 24$

4×6 is
4 more
than 20.

(c)

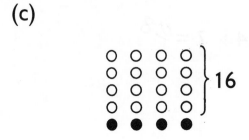

$4 \times 4 = 16$
$4 \times 5 = 20$

4×5 is
4 more
than 16.

(d)

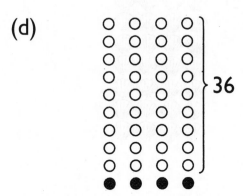

$4 \times 9 = 36$
$4 \times 10 = 40$

4×10 is
4 more
than 36.

2. Complete the multiplication sentences.

$4 \times 3 = 12$
$4 \times 4 = 16$

4×4 is 4 more than 12.

$4 \times 7 = 28$
$4 \times 8 = 30$

4×8 is 4 more than 28.

$4 \times 6 = 24$
$4 \times 7 = 28$

4×7 is 4 more than 24.

$4 \times 8 = 32$
$4 \times 9 = 34$

4×9 is 4 more than 32.

$4 \times 6 = 24$
$4 \times 5 = 20$

4×5 is 4 less than 24.

$4 \times 8 = 32$
$4 \times 7 = 28$

4×7 is 4 less than 32.

EXERCISE 16

1. Match the spaceships and the robots.

2. Mr. Smith planted 4 rows of trees.
   There were 5 trees in each row.
   How many trees were there altogether?

There were __2 0__ trees altogether.

___

3. The length of each side of the square is 6 cm.
   What is the total length of the 4 sides of the square?

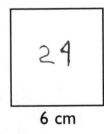

6 cm

___

4. 4 boys went fishing.
   Each boy caught 3 fish.
   How many fish did they catch altogether?

EXERCISE 17

1. Multiply.

4 × 2 → 8   14 ← 7 × 2

5 × 3 → 15   21 → 3 × 7

2 × 9 → 18   20 → 4 × 5

4 × 8 → 30   18 → 6 × 3

6 × 4 → 24   10 → 2 × 5

10 × 4 → 40   9 → 3 × 3

4 × 9 → 34   24 → 3 × 8

38

2. Mrs. Thomson bought 6 T-shirts.
   Each T-shirt cost $4.
   How much did Mrs. Thomson pay altogether?

   Mrs. Thomson paid $24 altogether.

3. Mrs. Wells bought 9 pieces of cloth.
   Each piece of cloth was 3 m long.
   How many meters of cloth did Mrs. Wells buy?

   It was 27 m long

4. Mrs. Coles bought 10 bottles of cooking oil.
   Each bottle contained 2 kg of cooking oil.
   How many kilograms of cooking oil did Mrs. Coles buy?

   She bought 20 kg of cooking oil

EXERCISE 18

1. Write the missing numbers.

$1 \times 4 = 4$

$4 \div 4 =$

$2 \times 4 = 8$

$8 \div 4 =$

$3 \times 4 = 12$

$12 \div 4 =$

$\times 4 = 16$

$16 \div 4 =$

$\times 4 = 20$

$20 \div 4 =$

$\times 4 = 24$

$24 \div 4 =$

$\times 4 = 40$

$40 \div 4 =$

$\times 4 = 28$

$28 \div 4 =$

$\times 4 = 36$

$36 \div 4 =$

$\times 4 = 32$

$32 \div 4 =$

2. Match the frogs and the tadpoles.

3. 36 children lined up in 4 equal rows.
   How many children were there in each row?

4. Larry bought 4 kg of grapes.
   He paid $24.
   What was the cost of 1 kg of grapes?

5. 4 pieces of ribbon are of the same length.
   Their total length is 28 m.
   How long is each piece of ribbon?

EXERCISE 19

1. Complete the multiplication sentences.

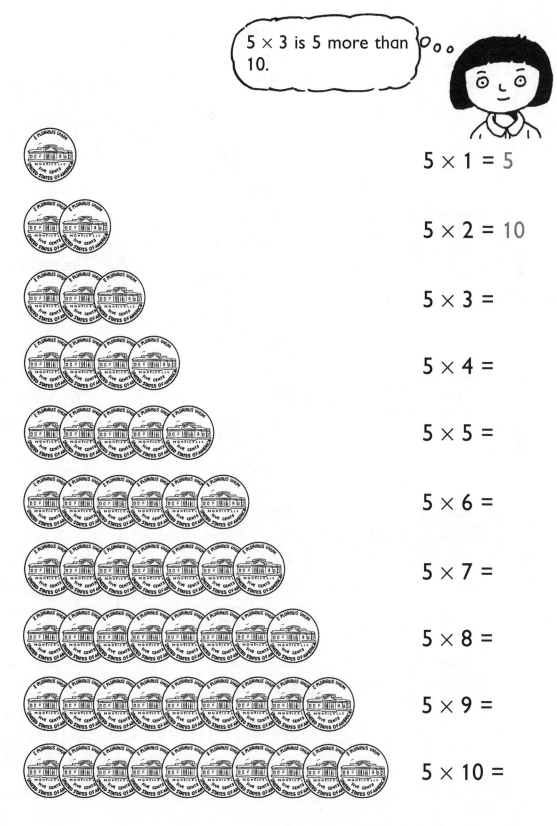

5 × 3 is 5 more than 10.

$5 \times 1 = 5$

$5 \times 2 = 10$

$5 \times 3 =$

$5 \times 4 =$

$5 \times 5 =$

$5 \times 6 =$

$5 \times 7 =$

$5 \times 8 =$

$5 \times 9 =$

$5 \times 10 =$

EXERCISE 20.

1. Match.

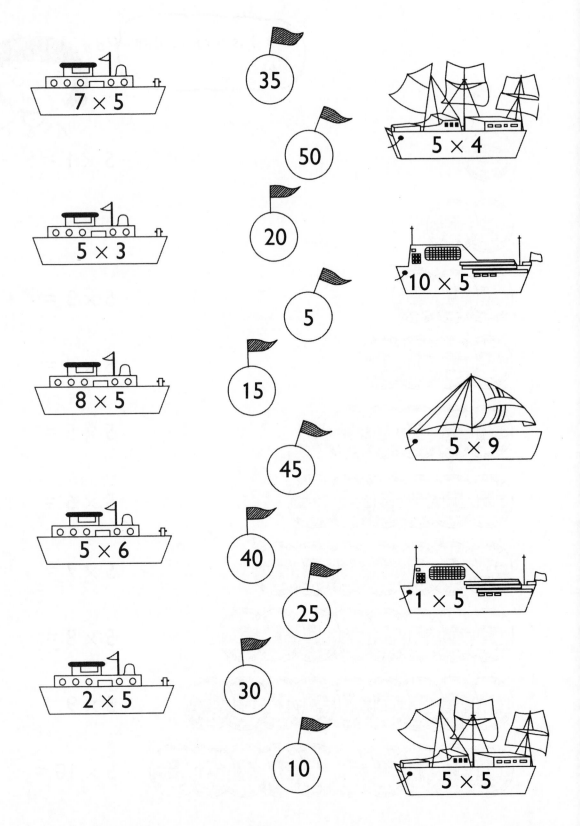

2. Mr. Goldman bought 5 boxes of cakes.
   There were 6 cakes in each box.
   How many cakes did he buy altogether?

---

3. Mrs. Cole made 3 pots of tea.
   She used 5 packets of sugar for each pot of tea.
   How many packets of sugar did she use altogether?

---

4. John spent $10 a week.
   How much did he spend in 4 weeks?

EXERCISE 21

1. Write the missing numbers.

$1 \times 5 = 5$

$5 \div 5 =$

$2 \times 5 = 10$

$10 \div 5 =$

$3 \times 5 = 15$

$15 \div 5 =$

$\times 5 = 35$

$35 \div 5 =$

$\times 5 = 25$

$25 \div 5 =$

$\times 5 = 45$

$45 \div 5 =$

$\times 5 = 20$

$20 \div 5 =$

$\times 5 = 30$

$30 \div 5 =$

$\times 5 = 40$

$40 \div 5 =$

$\times 5 = 50$

$50 \div 5 =$

2. Match the fish and hooks.

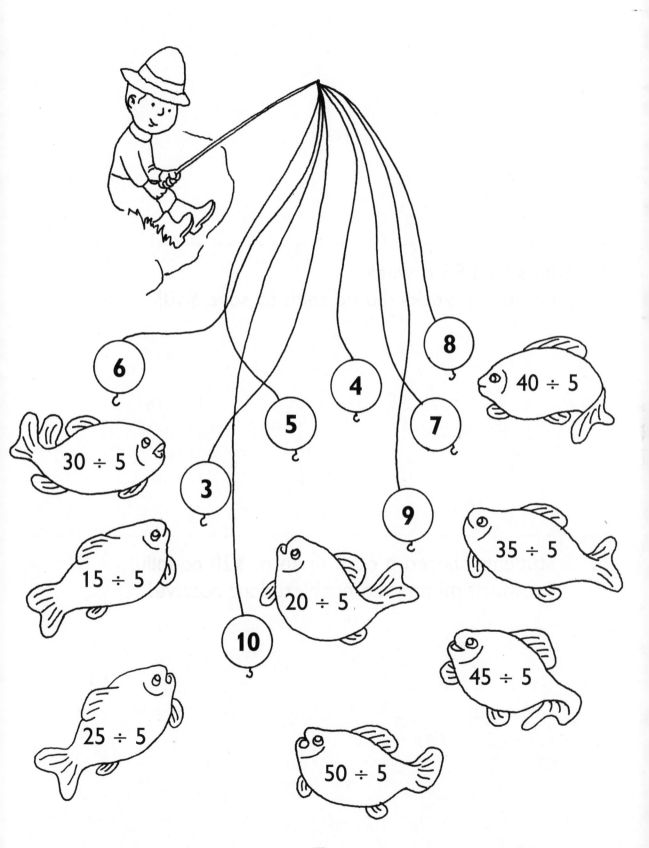

3. Lily tied 40 pencils into 5 equal bundles.
   How many pencils were there in each bundle?

---

4. Sam saved $5 a week.
   How many weeks did he take to save $50?

---

5. 5 students shared a cash prize of $20 equally.
   How much money did each student receive?

EXERCISE 22

1. Complete the multiplication sentences.

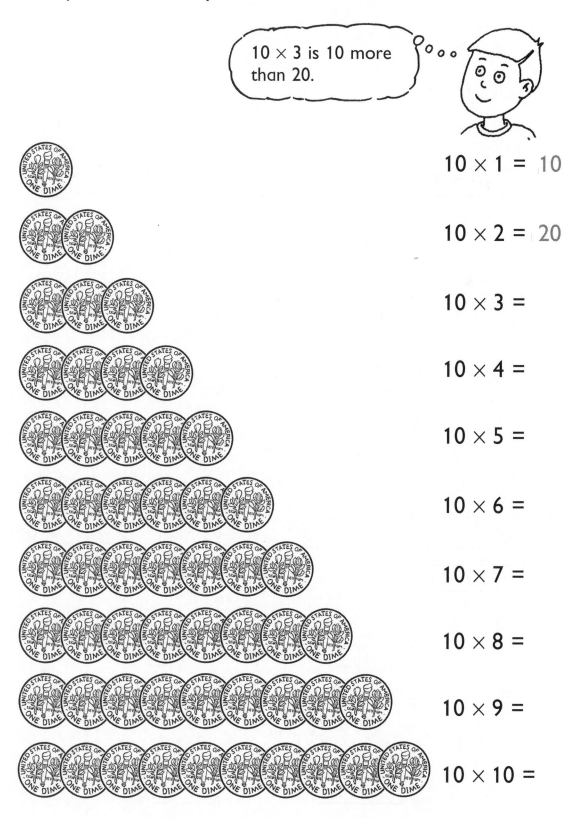

10 × 3 is 10 more than 20.

$10 \times 1 = 10$

$10 \times 2 = 20$

$10 \times 3 =$

$10 \times 4 =$

$10 \times 5 =$

$10 \times 6 =$

$10 \times 7 =$

$10 \times 8 =$

$10 \times 9 =$

$10 \times 10 =$

2. Multiply.

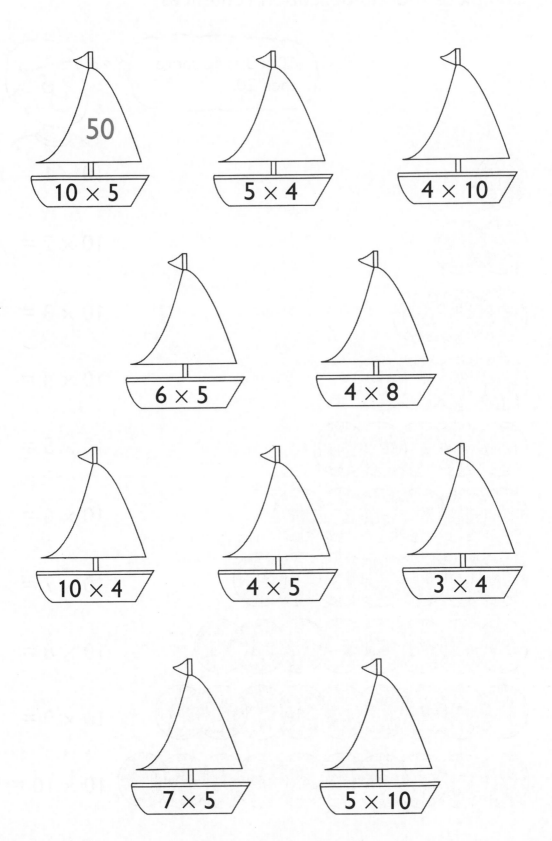

50 | 10 × 5

5 × 4

4 × 10

6 × 5

4 × 8

10 × 4

4 × 5

3 × 4

7 × 5

5 × 10

3. There are 5 soldiers in one row.
   How many soldiers are there in 10 rows?

---

4. A dictionary cost $10.
   Mr. Smith sold 10 copies of the dictionary.
   How much money did he receive?

---

5. Mrs. Wells bought 10 m of cloth to make dresses.
   1 m of cloth cost $7.
   How much did Mrs. Wells pay?

EXERCISE 23

1. Write the missing numbers.

$3 \times 10 = 30$	$30 \div 10 =$
$\times 10 = 50$	$50 \div 10 =$
$\times 10 = 60$	$60 \div 10 =$
$\times 10 = 70$	$70 \div 10 =$
$\times 10 = 10$	$10 \div 10 =$
$10 \times \quad = 30$	$30 \div 10 =$
$10 \times \quad = 80$	$80 \div 10 =$
$10 \times \quad = 40$	$40 \div 10 =$
$10 \times \quad = 20$	$20 \div 10 =$
$10 \times \quad = 90$	$90 \div 10 =$

2. Match each mother bird with its egg.

3. The total weight of 10 bags of flour is 60 kg.
   What is the weight of 1 bag of flour?

4. Mr. Goldman paid $40 for 10 potted plants.
   What was the cost of 1 potted plant?

5. Mrs. Thomson arranged 90 chairs in 10 rows.
   She put the same number of chairs in each row.
   How many chairs were there in each row?

REVIEW 2

1. Add or subtract.

(a) 237 + 99
 	
  =
	(b) 183 – 99
	
	  =

(c) 486 + 98
 	
  =
	(d) 304 – 98
	
	  =

(e) 699 + 99
 	
  =
	(f) 400 – 98
	
	  =

2. Write the missing numbers.

(a)
$$56 \xrightarrow{+\boxed{}} 100 \xrightarrow{+\boxed{}} 400$$

$$56 + \boxed{} = 400$$

$$400 - 56 = \boxed{}$$

(b)
$$78 \xrightarrow{+\boxed{}} 100 \xrightarrow{+\boxed{}} 140$$

$$78 + \boxed{} = 140$$

$$140 - 78 = \boxed{}$$

3. Multiply or divide.

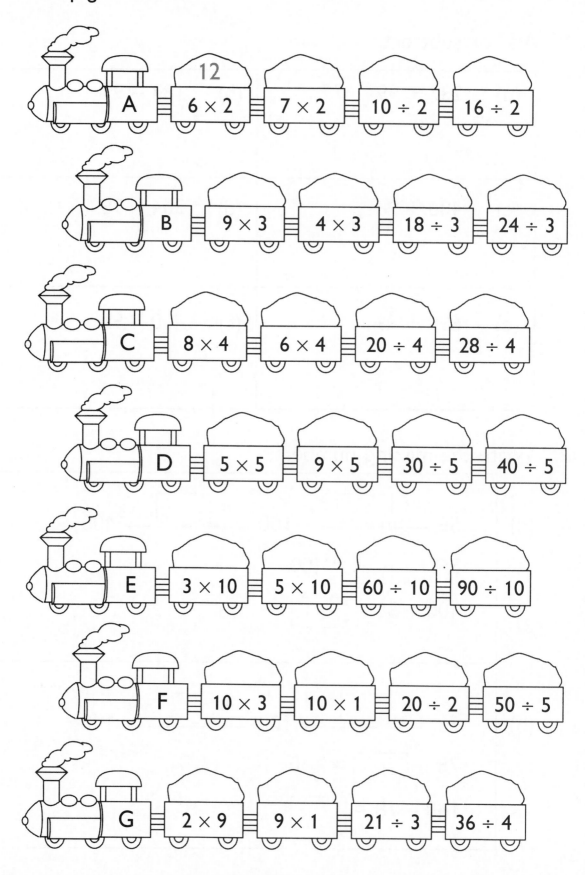

A
12
6 × 2 | 7 × 2 | 10 ÷ 2 | 16 ÷ 2

B
9 × 3 | 4 × 3 | 18 ÷ 3 | 24 ÷ 3

C
8 × 4 | 6 × 4 | 20 ÷ 4 | 28 ÷ 4

D
5 × 5 | 9 × 5 | 30 ÷ 5 | 40 ÷ 5

E
3 × 10 | 5 × 10 | 60 ÷ 10 | 90 ÷ 10

F
10 × 3 | 10 × 1 | 20 ÷ 2 | 50 ÷ 5

G
2 × 9 | 9 × 1 | 21 ÷ 3 | 36 ÷ 4

4. Mrs. Thomson sold 402 concert tickets in two days.
   She sold 382 tickets on the first day.
   How many tickets did she sell on the second day?

_____

5. Sam bought 3 boxes of pencils.
   There were 10 pencils in each box.
   How many pencils were there altogether?

_____

6. A boat can carry 5 people.
   How many boats are needed to carry 40 people?

7. 1 kg of papayas costs $5.
   What is the cost of 9 kg of papayas?

---

8. Mr. Coles has 122 letters to mail.
   He has only 86 envelopes.
   How many more envelopes does he need?

---

9. 386 boys, 255 girls and 145 adults were present at a school carnival.
   How many people were there altogether?

EXERCISE 24

1. Match the bags and the price tags.

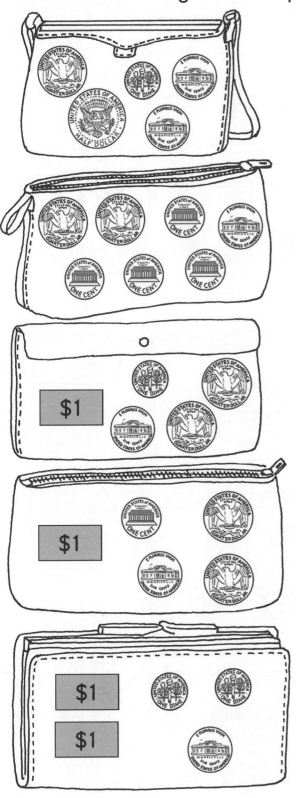

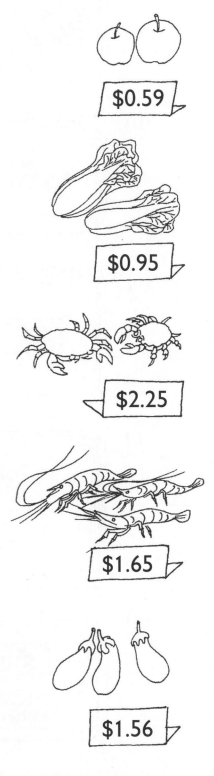

2. How much money is there in each of the following?

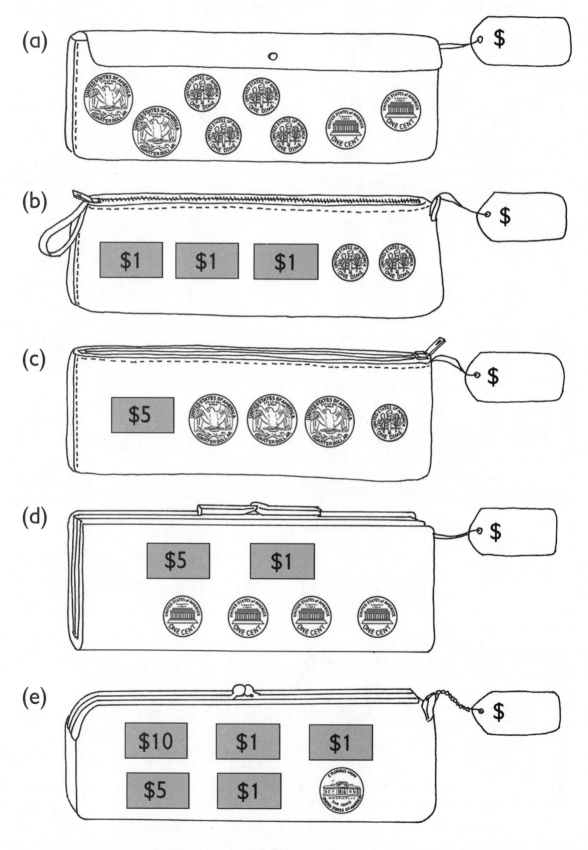

(a)

(b)

(c)

(d)

(e)

3. What is the cost of each item?

(a)

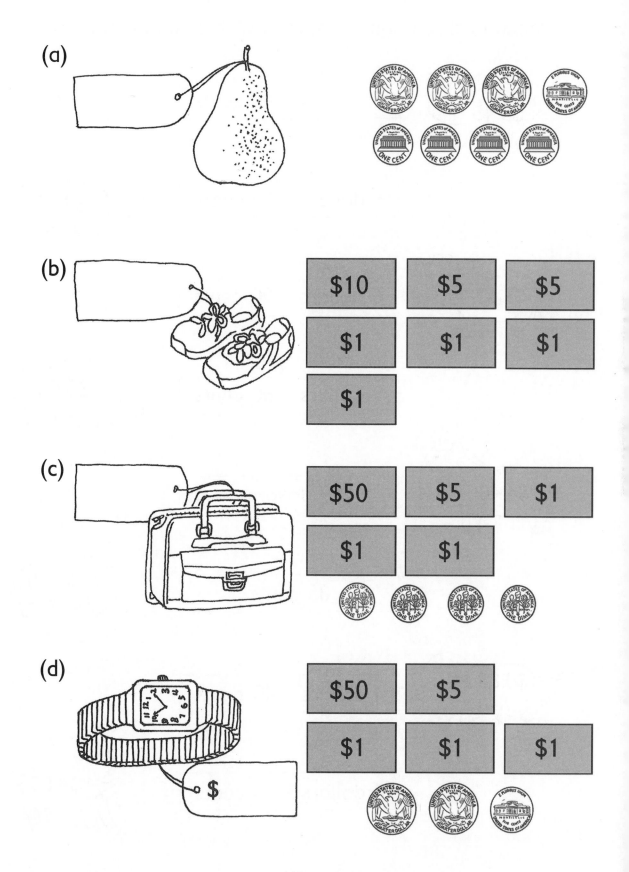

(b)

(c)

(d)

61

EXERCISE 25

1. Match each amount of money with a money-box.

$5.45

| 5 dollars   45 cents |

| 5 dollars   50 cents |

$9.60

$5.50

| 6 dollars   90 cents |

| 9 dollars   60 cents |

$8.00

$4.40

| 8 dollars |

| 85 cents |

$6.90

$0.85

| 4 dollars   40 cents |

| 4 dollars   5 cents |

$4.05

2. Write each amount of money in figures.

3 dollars 5 cents

4 dollars 30 cents

5 dollars

50 cents

9 dollars 75 cents

9 dollars 90 cents

3. Write the missing numbers.

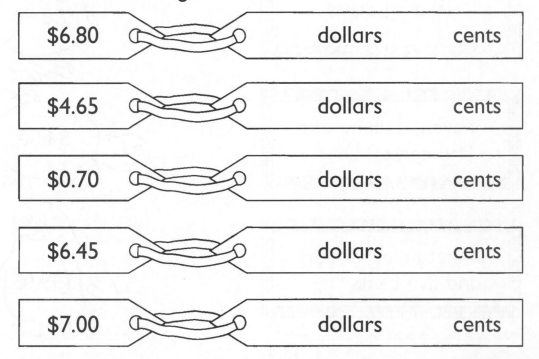

$6.80   _____ dollars _____ cents

$4.65   _____ dollars _____ cents

$0.70   _____ dollars _____ cents

$6.45   _____ dollars _____ cents

$7.00   _____ dollars _____ cents

EXERCISE 26

1. Match the amounts of money in words and in figures.

Twenty-three dollars

Four dollars

Thirteen dollars and thirty cents

Twenty cents

Seven dollars and fifty cents

Ninety-nine dollars and five cents

$0.20

$23.00

$7.50

$13.30

$4.00

$99.05

2. Write each amount of money in figures.

Fifteen cents	$0.15
Twenty dollars	
Forty-seven dollars	
Seventy-four dollars and fifty cents	
Thirty dollars and forty-five cents	
Eighty-six dollars and five cents	
Forty-seven dollars and fifteen cents	
Ninety-five cents	
Ninety-five dollars and five cents	
Forty dollars and twenty-five cents	

EXERCISE 27

1. Match the mice and the cheese.

2. Write in dollars.

100¢ = $ 1.00   205¢ = $ _____

200¢ = $ _____   190¢ = $ _____

125¢ = $ _____   350¢ = $ _____

240¢ = $ _____   85¢ = $ _____

360¢ = $ _____   70¢ = $ _____

405¢ = $ _____   5¢ = $ _____

3. Complete the tables.

30¢	$0.30
45¢	
120¢	
250¢	
300¢	
75¢	
345¢	
6¢	

$0.10	10¢
$0.75	
$1.05	
$3.05	
$2.50	
$1.50	
$4.00	
$0.08	

EXERCISE 28

1. How much money is needed to make $1?

(a)

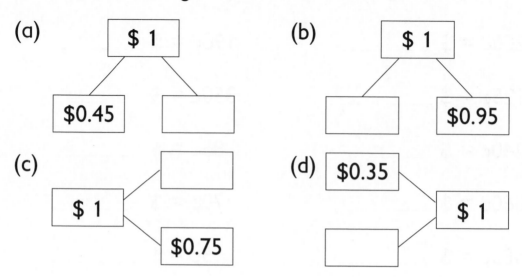

$ 1

$0.45   ☐

(b)

$ 1

☐ $0.95

(c)

☐

$ 1

$0.75

(d)

$0.35

$ 1

☐

2. Write the missing amount of money on each arrow.

$0.80

$0.40
$0.60

$0.70

$0.75

$1

$0.65

$0.85

$0.55

EXERCISE 29

1. How much money is needed to make $10?

(a)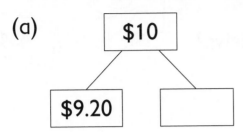

(b)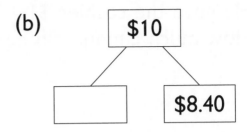

(c)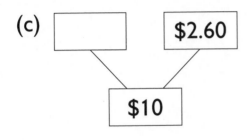

(d)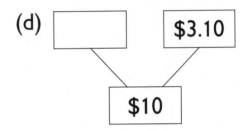

2. Write the missing numbers.

(a) $6.50 $\xrightarrow{\; + \boxed{}\, ¢\;}$ $7 $\xrightarrow{\; + \$\boxed{}\;}$ $10

$6.50 + $ $\boxed{}$ = $10

(b) $2.15 $\xrightarrow{\; + \boxed{}\, ¢\;}$ $3 $\xrightarrow{\; + \$\boxed{}\;}$ $10

$2.15 + $ $\boxed{}$ = $10

(c) $4.70 + $ $\boxed{}$ = $10

EXERCISE 30

1. Hassan bought this pencil sharpener.
    He gave the cashier $1.
    How much change did he receive?

    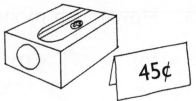

    45¢

2. Meiling had $10.
    She bought this vase.
    How much money did she have left?

    $5.20

3.

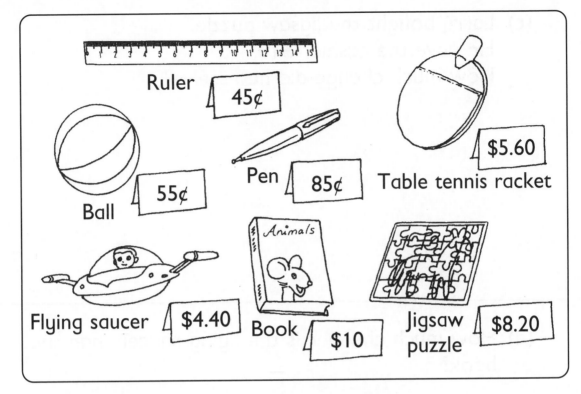

Ruler 45¢

Table tennis racket $5.60

Pen 85¢

Ball 55¢

Flying saucer $4.40

Book $10

Jigsaw puzzle $8.20

(a) Amy bought the ball and the ruler.
How much did she spend altogether?

(b) Mary had $1.
She bought the pen.
How much money did she have left?

71

(c) Larry bought the jigsaw puzzle.
He gave the cashier $10.
How much change did he receive?

(d) How much cheaper is the flying saucer than the book?

(e) Matthew bought two of the items.
He spent $10 altogether.
What did he buy?

EXERCISE 31

1. Add.

(a) $0.85 $\xrightarrow{\ +\ \$4\ }$ \$ [   ]

(b) $1.45 $\xrightarrow{\ +\ \$3\ }$ \$ [   ]

(c) $2.05 $\xrightarrow{\ +\ \$8\ }$ \$ [   ]

(d) $3.70 $\xrightarrow{\ +\ \$10\ }$ \$ [   ]

(e) $2.35 $\xrightarrow{\ +\ 20¢\ }$ \$ [   ]

(f) $1.25 $\xrightarrow{\ +\ 65¢\ }$ \$ [   ]

(g) $2.60 $\xrightarrow{\ +\ 15¢\ }$ \$ [   ]

(h) $3.75 $\xrightarrow{\ +\ 5¢\ }$ \$ [   ]

(i) $3.40 $\xrightarrow{\ +\ 60¢\ }$ \$ [   ]

(j) $2.75 $\xrightarrow{\ +\ 25¢\ }$ \$ [   ]

(k) $4.35 $\xrightarrow{\ +\ 65¢\ }$ \$ [   ]

(l) $4.45 $\xrightarrow{\ +\ 55¢\ }$ \$ [   ]

EXERCISE 32

1. Write the missing numbers.

(a) $1.45 $\xrightarrow{+ \ \$2}$ \$ [____] $\xrightarrow{+ \ 30¢}$ \$ [____]

$1.45 + $2.30 = \$ [____]

(b) $2.60 $\xrightarrow{+ \ \$3}$ \$ [____] $\xrightarrow{+ \ 25¢}$ \$ [____]

$2.60 + $3.25 = \$ [____]

(c) $3.15 $\xrightarrow{+ \ \$2}$ \$ [____] $\xrightarrow{+ \ 65¢}$ \$ [____]

$3.15 + $2.65 = \$ [____]

2. Add.

(a) $2.40 + $1.20 =
(b) $4.20 + $2.70 =
(c) $2.55 + $2.35 =
(d) $3.75 + $1.05 =
(e) $2.45 + $3.15 =
(f) $6.25 + $2.65 =

EXERCISE 33

1. Add.

$0.85 + $2.20 **E**	$3.60 + $1.85 **F**	$2.75 + $0.80 **L**
$7.75 +$0.60 **N**	$4.15 + $3.95 **O**	$5.25 + $3.95 **R**
$4.45 + $1.75 **S**	$2.95 + $3.05 **U**	$1.55 + $7.55 **W**

What is the name of this flower?

Write the letters in the boxes below to find out.

							E	
$6.20	$6.00	$8.35	$5.45	$3.55	$8.10	$9.10	$3.05	$9.20

75

EXERCISE 34

1. Add.

(a) $2.45 + $0.99 =
(b) $4.15 + $3.99 =
(c) $3.55 + $1.99 =
(d) $3.25 + $2.99 =

2. Add.

(a) $3.80 + $0.95 =
(b) $2.65 + $0.95 =
(c) $3.40 + $2.95 =
(d) $4.35 + $3.95 =

EXERCISE 35

1. Subtract.

(a) $4.85 $\xrightarrow{\;-\;\$3\;}$ $ ☐

(b) $6.45 $\xrightarrow{\;-\;\$2\;}$ $ ☐

(c) $7.05 $\xrightarrow{\;-\;\$4\;}$ $ ☐

(d) $9.25 $\xrightarrow{\;-\;\$8\;}$ $ ☐

(e) $2.95 $\xrightarrow{\;-\;60¢\;}$ $ ☐

(f) $5.75 $\xrightarrow{\;-\;70¢\;}$ $ ☐

(g) $6.40 $\xrightarrow{\;-\;40¢\;}$ $ ☐

(h) $9.80 $\xrightarrow{\;-\;65¢\;}$ $ ☐

(i) $4 $\xrightarrow{\;-\;80¢\;}$ $ ☐

(j) $5 $\xrightarrow{\;-\;70¢\;}$ $ ☐

(k) $3 $\xrightarrow{\;-\;55¢\;}$ $ ☐

(l) $6 $\xrightarrow{\;-\;75¢\;}$ $ ☐

EXERCISE 36

1. Write the missing numbers.

(a) $6.80 $\xrightarrow{-\ \$2}$ $ [ ] $\xrightarrow{-\ 50¢}$ $ [ ]

$6.80 – $2.50 = $ [ ]

(b) $4.75 $\xrightarrow{-\ \$3}$ $ [ ] $\xrightarrow{-\ 35¢}$ $ [ ]

$4.75 – $3.35 = $ [ ]

(c) $5.90 $\xrightarrow{-\ \$3}$ $ [ ] $\xrightarrow{-\ 65¢}$ $ [ ]

$5.90 – $3.65 = $ [ ]

2. Subtract.

(a) $4.80 – $1.20 =
(b) $5.85 – $2.60 =
(c) $5.90 – $3.75 =
(d) $6.70 – $2.35 =
(e) $4.50 – $2.05 =
(f) $7.70 – $3.45 =

EXERCISE 37

1. Subtract.

$2.25 − $0.60 **A**	$3.10 − $0.55 **D**	$5.00 − $0.25 **F**
$7.00 −$4.70 **G**	$6.35 − $3.50 **L**	$7.05 − $2.45 **N**
$8.50 − $5.90 **O**	$4.30 − $3.85 **R**	$9.20 − $7.65 **Y**

What is the name of this insect?

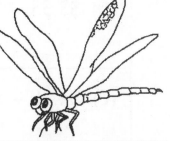

Write the letters in the boxes below to find out.

		A						
$2.55	$0.45	$1.65	$2.30	$2.60	$4.60	$4.75	$2.85	$1.55

EXERCISE 38

1. Subtract.

    (a) $4.30 – $0.99 =

    (b) $3.45 – $0.99 =

    (c) $4.25 – $1.99 =

    (d) $6.00 – $2.99 =

2. Subtract.

    (a) $2.20 – $0.95 =

    (b) $3.55 – $0.95 =

    (c) $4.10 – $3.95 =

    (d) $8.25 – $5.95 =

EXERCISE 39

1. Molly bought a ball for $2.40.
   She also bought a toy airplane for $3.25.
   How much did she spend altogether?

2. Sam had $8.
   He bought a toy car for $5.35.
   How much money did he have left?

3. A toy robot costs $5.90.
   A doll costs $3.85.
   How much cheaper is the doll?

4. Sufen bought this set of stamps from a post office.
   She had $6.30 left.
   How much money did she have at first?

5. Minghui spent $2.60 on his lunch.
   His brother spent $0.95 more than he.
   How much did his brother spend?

6. Lily saved $10.
   She saved $1.95 more than Alice.
   How much did Alice save?

REVIEW 3

1. Write the numbers.

    (a) | Four hundred fifty-one

    (b) | Nine hundred sixty

2. (a) What number is 1 less than 1000? _____

    (b) What number is 10 more than 690? _____

    (c) What number is 100 more than 808? _____

3. Fill in the blanks with **m** or **cm**.

    (a) The height of a door is about 3 _____.

    (b) Lily is 3 _____ shorter than her brother.

    (c) A pencil is about 19 _____ long.

    (d) Gary took part in a 400-_____ race.

4. Fill in the blanks with **kg** or **g**.

    (a) A watermelon weighs about 2 _____.

    (b) A pear weighs about 120 _____.

    (c) Mr. Banks buys a jar of honey that weighs
        850 _____.

    (d) Mark bought a 5-_____ bag of rice.

5. Add or subtract.

(a) 369 + 631 =	(b) 722 − 458 =
(c) $3.85 + $2.05 =	(d) $4.25 − $1.45 =
(e) $4.55 + $0.99 =	(f) $10 − $2.95 =

6. Write the missing numbers.

(a)   3 ×   = 21   21 ÷ 3 =

(b)   × 4 = 32   32 ÷ 4 =

(c)   5 ×   = 45   45 ÷ 5 =

(d)   × 10 = 80   80 ÷ 10 =

7. Mrs. Lambert bought 8 packets of pens.
   There were 3 pens in each packet.
   How many pens did she buy?

8. A boy cut 20 m of rope into 5 equal pieces.
   Find the length of each piece of rope.

9. Ryan bought a storybook for $5.35.
   He gave the cashier $10.
   How much change did he receive?

10. The total weight of a papaya and a pear is 920 g.
The pear weighs 135 g.
Find the weight of the papaya.

11. The tigers in a zoo are fed 6 kg of meat a day.
How many kilograms of meat are needed to feed the tigers for 4 days?

12. A calculator costs $9.50.
A pen is $1.60 cheaper than the calculator.
Find the cost of the pen.

REVIEW 4

1. Complete the tables.

(a) A triangle has 3 sides.

Number of triangles	1	2	3	6	8
Number of sides	3				

(b) There are 4 pears in a bag.

Number of bags	2	5	8	9	10
Number of pears	8				

(c) A flower has 5 petals.

Number of flowers	2	3	4	6	7
Number of petals	10				

(d) There are 10 pencils in a box.

Number of boxes	3	4	5	7	9
Number of pencils					

2. Fill in the missing numbers.

(a) 345 $\xrightarrow{\ +\ 60\ }$ ☐ $\xrightarrow{\ +\ 8\ }$ ☐

(b) 506 $\xrightarrow{\ +\ 90\ }$ ☐ $\xrightarrow{\ +\ 4\ }$ ☐

(c) 472 $\xrightarrow{\ -\ 70\ }$ ☐ $\xrightarrow{\ -\ 4\ }$ ☐

(d) 926 $\xrightarrow{\ -\ 60\ }$ ☐ $\xrightarrow{\ -\ 8\ }$ ☐

3. Add or subtract.

(a) 476 + 30 =	(b) 700 + 7 =
(c) 882 – 80 =	(d) 400 – 6 =

4. Subtract.

(a) $1 – $0.60 =	(b) $10 – $9.20 =
(c) $1 – $0.45 =	(d) $10 – $7.85 =

5.

A

B

There is $_____ more in Bag A than in Bag B.

6. Sarina, Sue, Rosa and Molly spent **$36** on lunch.
   They shared the cost equally.
   How much did each of them pay?

---

7. Cameron bought 6 T-shirts.
   How much did he pay altogether?

$4

---

8. Mr. Givens packed 45 kg of sugar into bags.
   Each bag of sugar weighed 5 kg.
   How many bags of sugar were there?

9. Mrs. Coles bought 19 mangoes.
   Mrs. Lambert bought 28 mangoes.
   How many more mangoes did Mrs. Lambert buy than
   Mrs. Coles?

---

10. Matthew learns to spell 7 words every week.
    How many words does he learn to spell in 5 weeks?

---

11. The students in a class borrowed 26 books from the
    class library.
    There were 34 books left.
    How many books were there in the library at first?

EXERCISE 40

1. Check (✓) the pictures which show $\frac{1}{2}$.

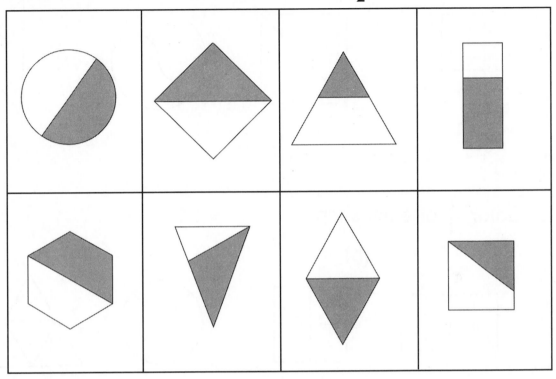

2. Check (✓) the pictures which show $\frac{1}{4}$.

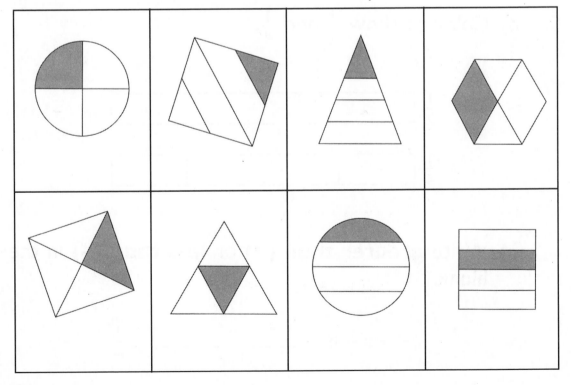

3. Color $\frac{1}{2}$ of each shape.

   (a) 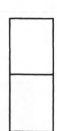   (b) 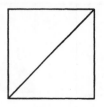   (c) 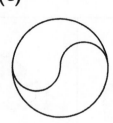   (d)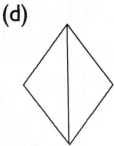

4. Color $\frac{1}{4}$ of each shape.

   (a) 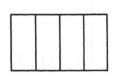   (b)   (c)    (d)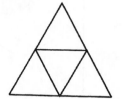

5. (a) Color to show $\frac{1}{2}$ and $\frac{1}{4}$.

   $\frac{1}{2}$ [bar divided into 2]

   $\frac{1}{4}$ [bar divided into 4]

   (b) Write **greater than (>)** or **less than (<)** in the blank.

   $\frac{1}{2}$ is _____ $\frac{1}{4}$.

EXERCISE 41

1. Fill in the blanks with fractions.

(a) 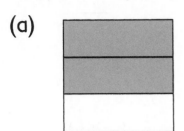   The square is divided into 3 equal parts.
2 out of the 3 equal parts are shaded.

_____ of the square is shaded.

(b) 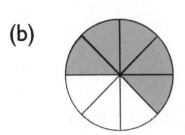   The circle is divided into 8 equal parts.
5 out of the 8 equal parts are shaded.

_____ of the circle is shaded.

(c) 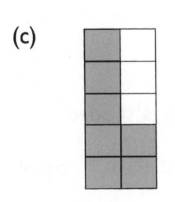   The rectangle is divided into 10 equal parts.
7 out of the 10 equal parts are shaded.

_____ of the rectangle is shaded.

(d) 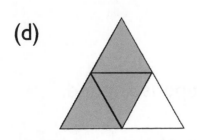   The triangle is divided into 4 equal parts.
3 out of the 4 equal parts are shaded.

_____ of the triangle is shaded.

2. (a)

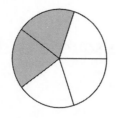

$\frac{1}{6}$ of the shape is shaded.

$\frac{1}{6}$ is ☐ out of the ☐ equal parts.

(b)

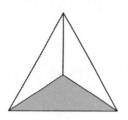

$\frac{2}{5}$ of the shape is shaded.

$\frac{2}{5}$ is ☐ out of the ☐ equal parts.

(c)

$\frac{1}{3}$ of the shape is shaded.

$\frac{1}{3}$ is ☐ out of the ☐ equal parts.

(d)

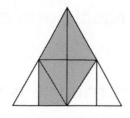

$\frac{3}{4}$ of the shape is shaded.

$\frac{3}{4}$ is ☐ out of the ☐ equal parts.

(e)

$\frac{5}{8}$ of the shape is shaded.

$\frac{5}{8}$ is ☐ out of the ☐ equal parts.

EXERCISE 42

1. What fraction of each circle is shaded?
    Match the circles to the correct answers.

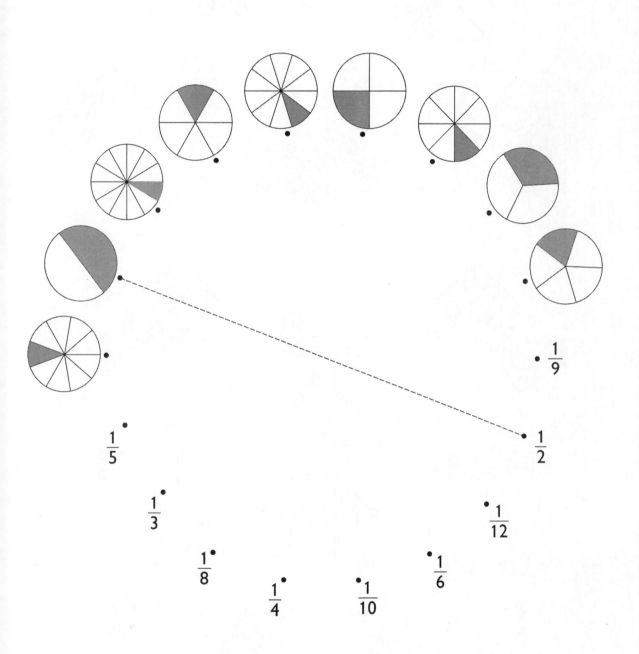

2. What fraction of each shape is shaded?
   Match the shapes to the correct answers.

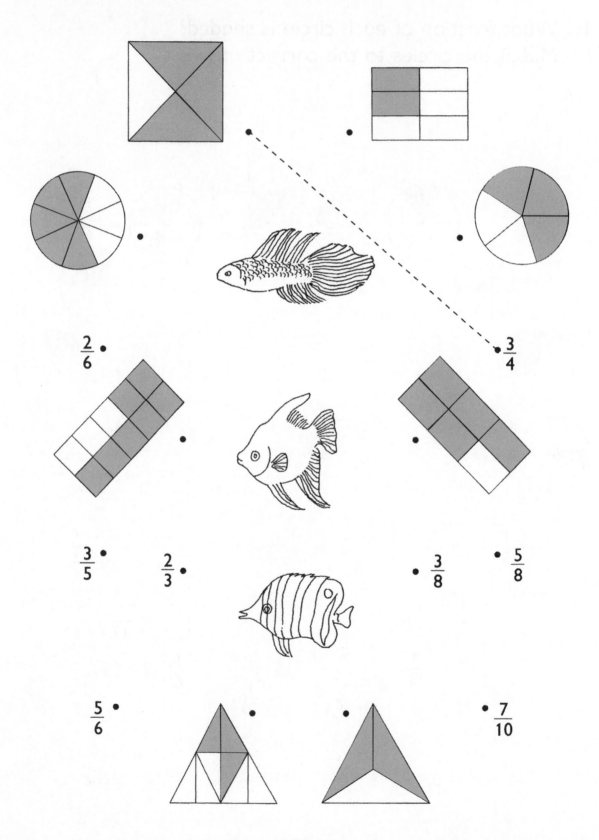

3. What fraction of each shape is shaded?

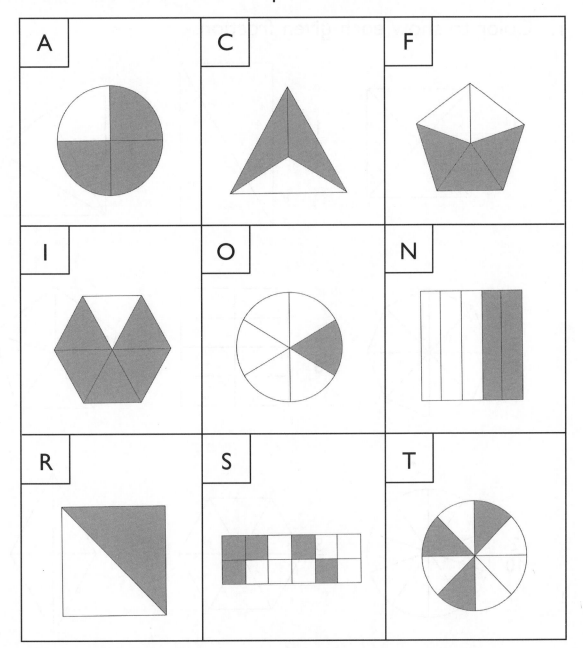

What do you call the numbers $\frac{1}{2}$ and $\frac{1}{4}$?

Write the letters which match the answers to find out.

		A						
$\frac{3}{5}$	$\frac{1}{2}$	$\frac{3}{4}$	$\frac{2}{3}$	$\frac{3}{8}$	$\frac{5}{6}$	$\frac{1}{6}$	$\frac{2}{5}$	$\frac{5}{12}$

EXERCISE 43

1. Color to show each given fraction.

$\frac{1}{4}$ 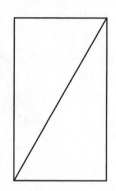 $\frac{1}{2}$ 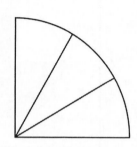 $\frac{2}{3}$

$\frac{3}{8}$ 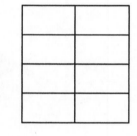 $\frac{7}{8}$ 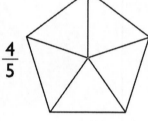 $\frac{4}{5}$

$\frac{2}{10}$ 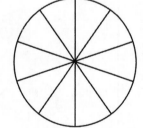 $\frac{5}{6}$ 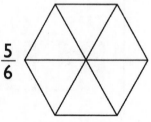 $\frac{3}{4}$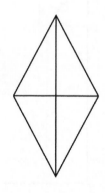

$\frac{2}{5}$  $\frac{3}{6}$ 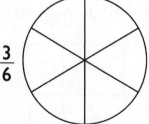 $\frac{9}{10}$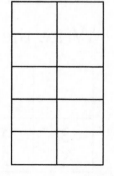

EXERCISE 44

1. Color one part of each bar to show the given fraction.

$\frac{1}{2}$

$\frac{1}{3}$

$\frac{1}{4}$

$\frac{1}{5}$

$\frac{1}{6}$

$\frac{1}{8}$

$\frac{1}{10}$

$\frac{1}{12}$

2. Write **greater than (>)** or **less than (<)** in the blank. (Use the fraction bars above to help you.)

(a) $\frac{1}{2}$ is _____ $\frac{1}{3}$. (b) $\frac{1}{6}$ is _____ $\frac{1}{2}$.

(c) $\frac{1}{8}$ is _____ $\frac{1}{2}$. (d) $\frac{1}{3}$ is _____ $\frac{1}{6}$.

(e) $\frac{1}{12}$ is _____ $\frac{1}{2}$. (f) $\frac{1}{5}$ is _____ $\frac{1}{10}$.

3. Circle the greater fraction.

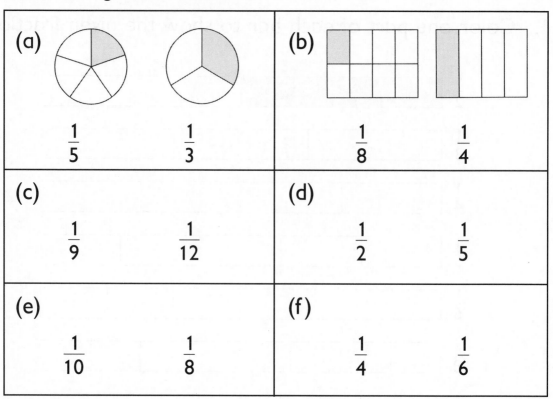

(a) $\frac{1}{5}$ $\frac{1}{3}$

(b) $\frac{1}{8}$ $\frac{1}{4}$

(c) $\frac{1}{9}$ $\frac{1}{12}$

(d) $\frac{1}{2}$ $\frac{1}{5}$

(e) $\frac{1}{10}$ $\frac{1}{8}$

(f) $\frac{1}{4}$ $\frac{1}{6}$

4. Circle the smaller fraction.

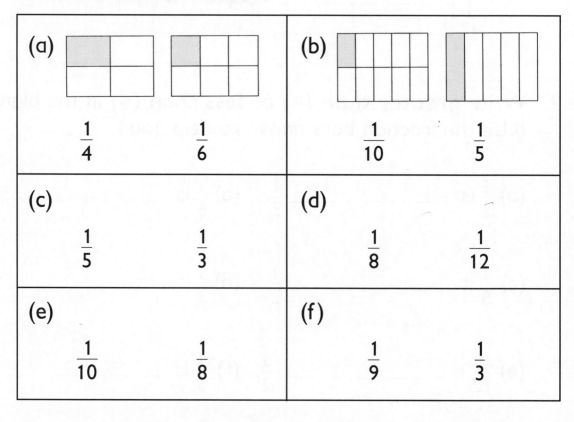

(a) $\frac{1}{4}$ $\frac{1}{6}$

(b) $\frac{1}{10}$ $\frac{1}{5}$

(c) $\frac{1}{5}$ $\frac{1}{3}$

(d) $\frac{1}{8}$ $\frac{1}{12}$

(e) $\frac{1}{10}$ $\frac{1}{8}$

(f) $\frac{1}{9}$ $\frac{1}{3}$

5. Circle the greatest fraction.

(a) $\frac{1}{3}$, $\frac{1}{2}$, $\frac{1}{4}$

(b) $\frac{1}{7}$, $\frac{1}{8}$, $\frac{1}{5}$

(c) $\frac{1}{8}$, $\frac{1}{6}$, $\frac{1}{4}$

(d) $\frac{1}{7}$, $\frac{1}{5}$, $\frac{1}{6}$

6. Circle the smallest fraction.

(a) $\frac{1}{5}$, $\frac{1}{7}$, $\frac{1}{2}$

(b) $\frac{1}{10}$, $\frac{1}{12}$, $\frac{1}{8}$

(c) $\frac{1}{4}$, $\frac{1}{3}$, $\frac{1}{2}$

(d) $\frac{1}{9}$, $\frac{1}{6}$, $\frac{1}{3}$

7. Arrange the fractions in order, beginning with the smallest.

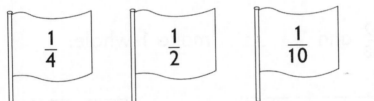

$\frac{1}{4}$ $\frac{1}{2}$ $\frac{1}{10}$ $\frac{1}{8}$

_____

8. Arrange the fractions in order, beginning with the biggest.

$\frac{1}{9}$ $\frac{1}{12}$ $\frac{1}{3}$ $\frac{1}{5}$

_____

EXERCISE 45

1. Fill in the blanks.

(a)

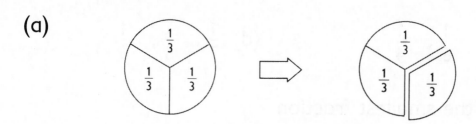

$\frac{1}{3}$ and _____ make 1 whole.

(b)

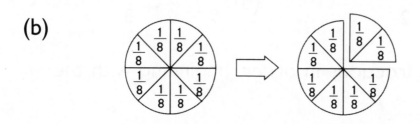

$\frac{2}{8}$ and _____ make 1 whole.

(c)

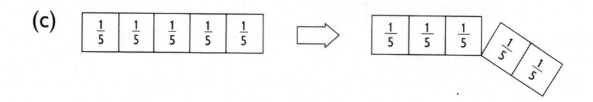

$\frac{2}{5}$ and _____ make 1 whole.

(d)

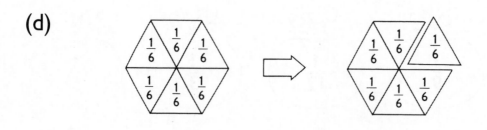

$\frac{1}{6}$ and _____ make 1 whole.

102

2. Join each pair of fractions that add up to 1.

EXERCISE 46

1. Count in steps of 5 minutes.
    Write the missing numbers.

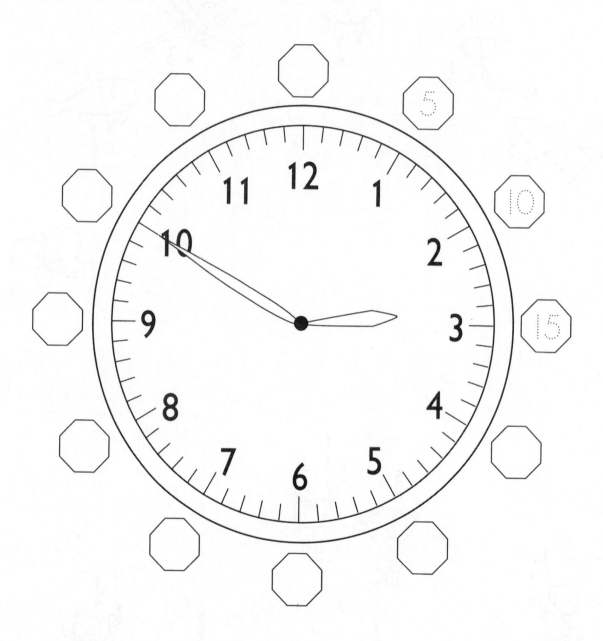

The time is _____ minutes after 2 o'clock.

2. Write the time shown on each clock face.

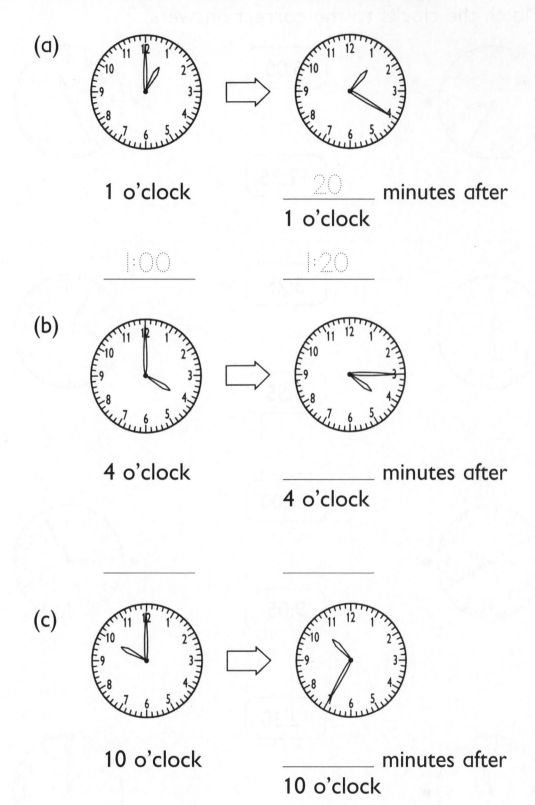

(a)

1 o'clock

_____20_____ minutes after
1 o'clock

_____1:00_____   _____1:20_____

(b)

4 o'clock

_____ minutes after
4 o'clock

_____   _____

(c)

10 o'clock

_____ minutes after
10 o'clock

_____   _____

3. What time is shown on each clock face?
   Match the clocks to the correct answers.

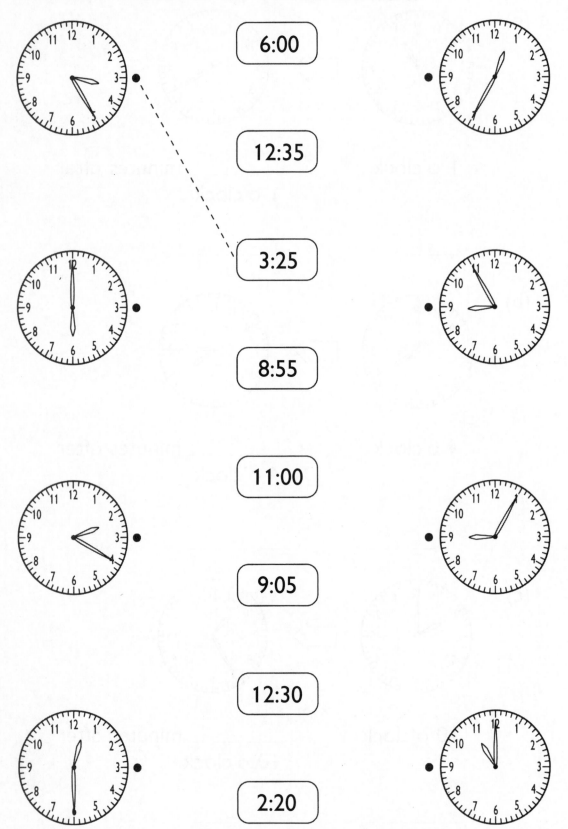

6:00

12:35

3:25

8:55

11:00

9:05

12:30

2:20

4. What time is it?

7:30

_____

_____

_____

_____

_____

_____

_____

_____

_____

_____

_____

_____

EXERCISE 47

1. Fill in the blanks.

(a)

_____ minutes after _____ o'clock

_____ minutes past _____

(b)

_____ minutes after _____ o'clock

_____ minutes past _____

(c)

_____ minutes before _____ o'clock

_____ minutes to _____

(d)

_____ minutes before _____ o'clock

_____ minutes to _____

2. Fill in the blanks.

(a)

6:10

_____ minutes past _____

(b)

6:45

_____ minutes to _____

(c)

7:15

_____ minutes past _____

(d)

7:35

_____ minutes to _____

3. Draw the minute hand on each clock face to show the time.

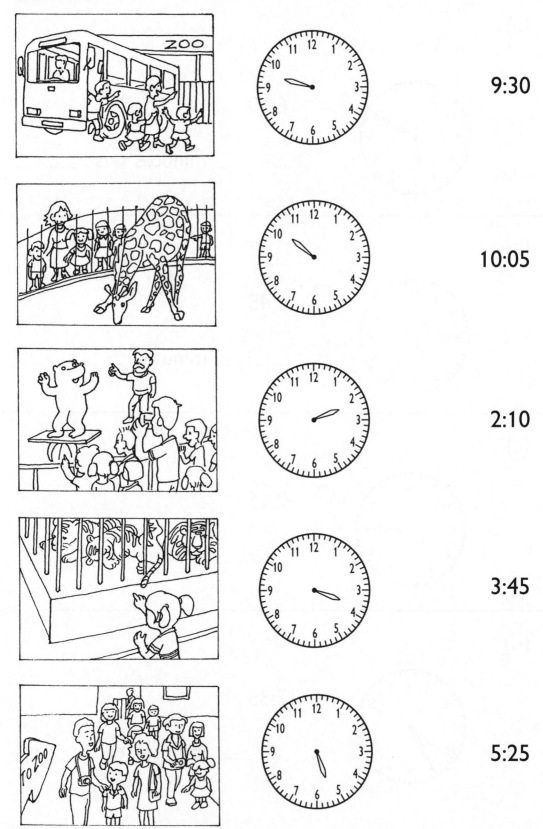

9:30

10:05

2:10

3:45

5:25

EXERCISE 48

1. Fill in the blanks.

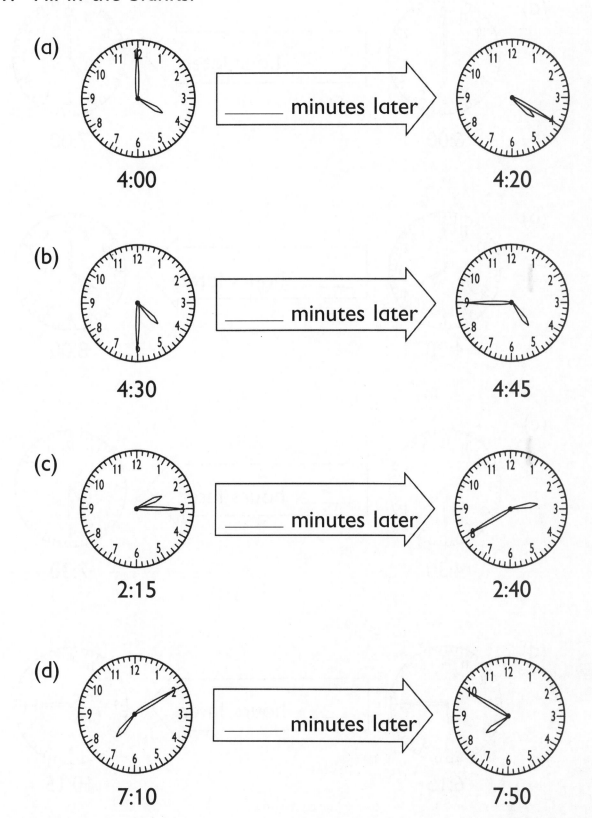

(a)

4:00 → _____ minutes later → 4:20

(b)

4:30 → _____ minutes later → 4:45

(c)

2:15 → _____ minutes later → 2:40

(d)

7:10 → _____ minutes later → 7:50

111

2. Fill in the blanks.

(a)

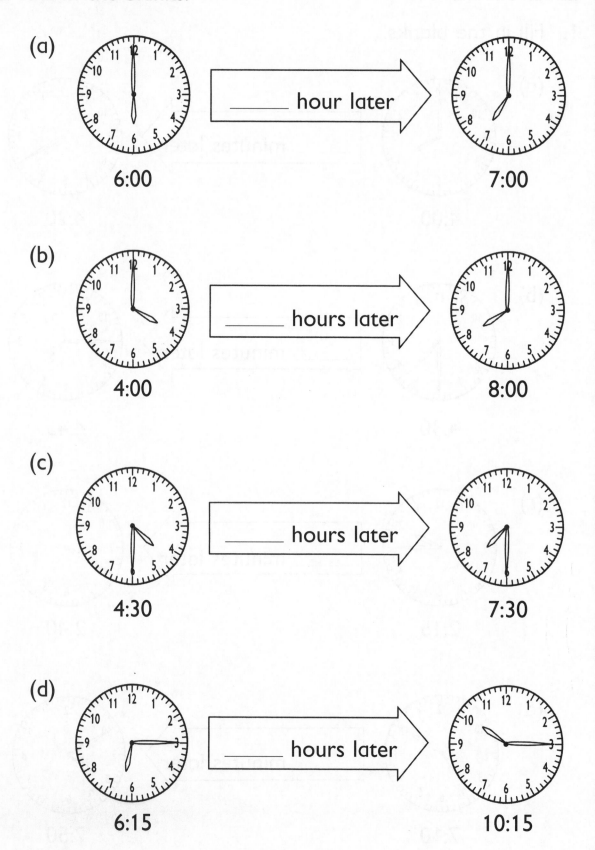

6:00   _____ hour later   7:00

(b)

4:00   _____ hours later   8:00

(c)

4:30   _____ hours later   7:30

(d)

6:15   _____ hours later   10:15

112

3. Fill in the blanks.

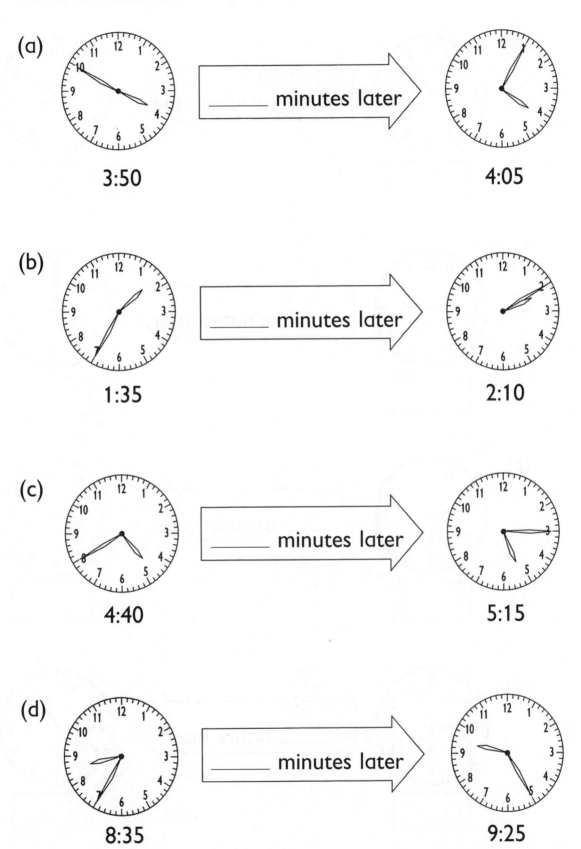

(a)

3:50   _____ minutes later   4:05

(b)

1:35   _____ minutes later   2:10

(c)

4:40   _____ minutes later   5:15

(d)

8:35   _____ minutes later   9:25

4. Complete each of the following:

(a)
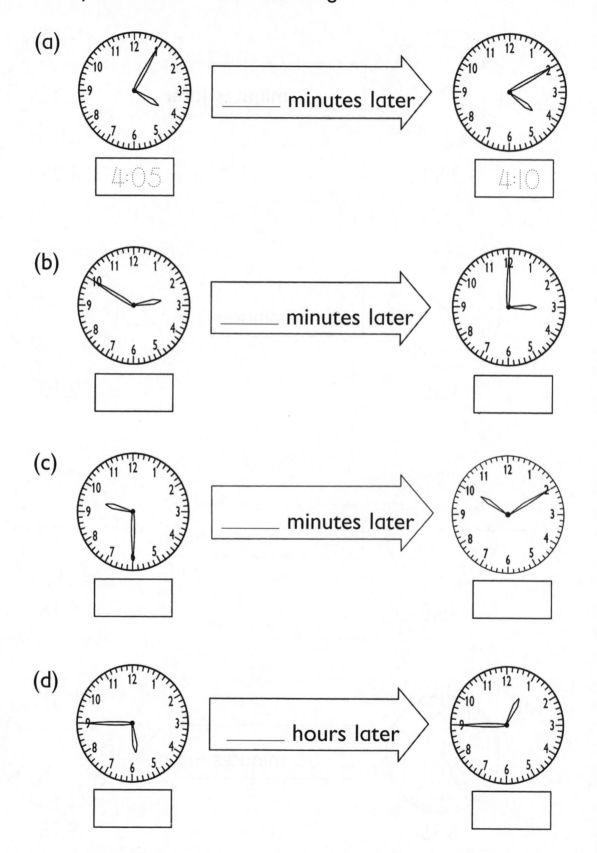

_____ minutes later

4:05   4:10

(b)

_____ minutes later

(c)

_____ minutes later

(d)

_____ hours later

EXERCISE 49

1. Fill in the blanks.

(a)

The time is 4:15 a.m.
20 minutes later, it will be _____.

(b)

The time is 11:35 p.m.
15 minutes later, it will be _____.

(c)

The time is 5:45 a.m.
30 minutes later, it will be _____.

(d)

The time is 5:20 p.m.
40 minutes later, it will be _____.

(e)

The time is 2:40 a.m.
35 minutes later, it will be _____.

2. Fill in the blanks.

(a)

The time is 3:25 p.m.

2 hours later, it will be _____.

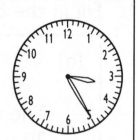

(b)

The time is 1:15 a.m.

3 hours later, it will be _____.

(c)

The time is 10:40 a.m.

3 hours later, it will be _____.

(d)

The time is 7:10 p.m.

5 hours later, it will be _____.

(e)

The time is 10:55 p.m.

4 hours later, it will be _____.

REVIEW 5

1. Write the missing numbers.

   (a) $500 + 60 + 9 = \boxed{}$

   (b) $\boxed{} + 70 + 8 = 778$

   (c) $844 - 400 = \boxed{}$

   (d) $309 - \boxed{} = 9$

2. Fill in the blanks.

   (a) 200 is _____ more than 160.

   (b) 84 is _____ less than 100.

   (c) _____ is 3 hundreds more than 526.

   (d) _____ is 5 tens less than 754.

3. Follow the arrows and find the missing numbers.

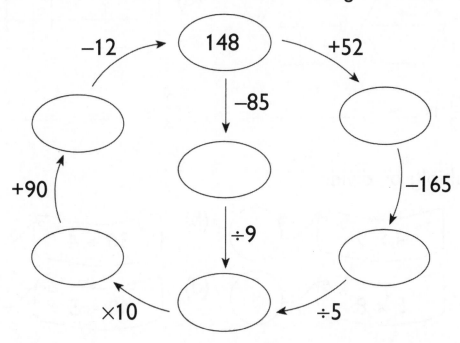

117

4. Add or subtract.

(a) $7.65 + $1.35 =
(b) $3.95 + $2.45 =
(c) $5.10 − $1.75 =
(d) $6.05 − $2.95 =

5. Color to show each pair of fractions.
    Then write **greater than (>)**, **less than (<)** or
    equal to (=) in the blank.

    (a)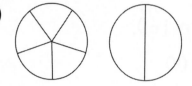

    $\frac{1}{5}$ is _____ $\frac{1}{2}$.

    (b)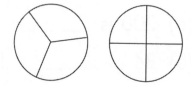

    $\frac{1}{3}$ is _____ $\frac{1}{4}$.

    (c)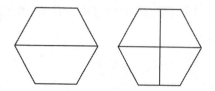

    $\frac{1}{2}$ is _____ $\frac{2}{4}$.

    (d)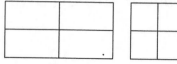

    $\frac{3}{4}$ is _____ $\frac{3}{8}$.

6. Multiply or divide.

    (a)  4 × 9

    (b)  36 ÷ 4

    (c)  5 × 8

    (d)  40 ÷ 5

7. Fill in the blanks.

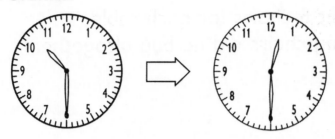

A concert started at 10:30 a.m. and ended at 12:30 p.m.

12:30 p.m. is _____ hours after 10:30 a.m.

8.

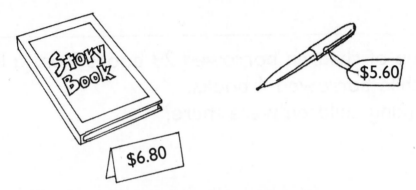

(a) Kevin bought the book and the pen.
How much did he spend altogether?

(b) After buying the book and the pen, Kevin had
$15 left.
How much money did he have at first?

9. Jeff bought 9 tables.
   He bought 5 chairs for each table.
   How many chairs did he buy altogether?

---

10. A group of children borrowed 20 books from a library.
    Each child borrowed 4 books.
    How many children were there?

---

11. 38 teachers, 298 boys and 162 girls went jogging.
    How many people went jogging altogether?

EXERCISE 50

1. Which container holds more water?
   Circle it.

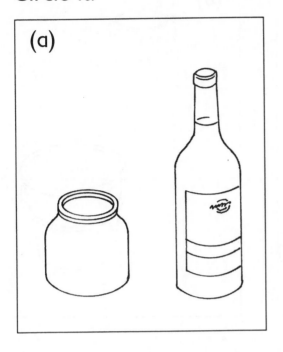

(a)

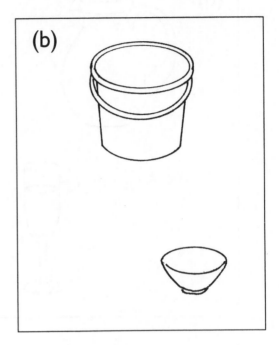

(b)

2. Which container holds the most water?
   Circle it.

(a)

(b)

3. Which container holds less water?
   Circle it.

(a)

(b)

4. Which container holds the least water?
   Circle it.

(a)

(b)

EXERCISE 51

1. Which container holds more water?

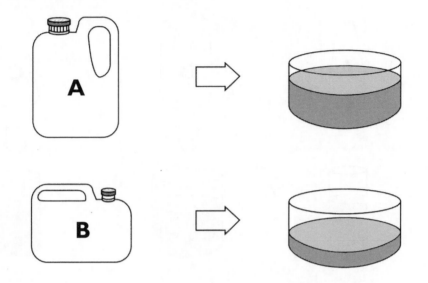

Container _____ holds more water than

Container _____.

2. Which container holds less water?

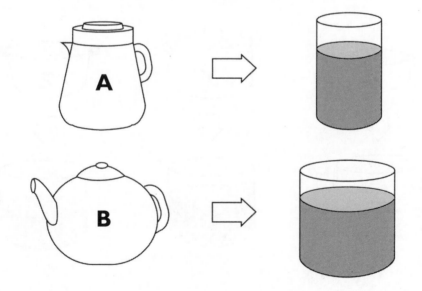

Container _____ holds less water than

Container _____.

3. Which container holds the most water?

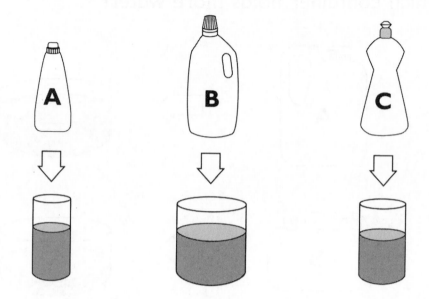

Container _____ holds the most water.

4. Which container holds the least water?

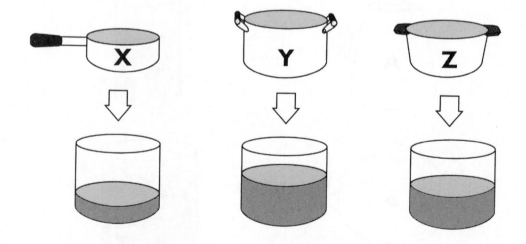

Container _____ holds the least water.

5. Fill in the blanks.

(a)

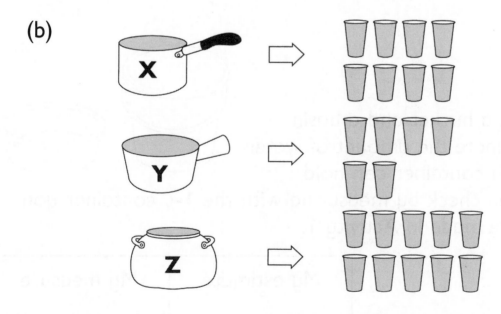

Glass _____ holds the most water.

Glass _____ holds the least water.

(b)

Pot X holds _____ cups of water more than Pot Y.

Pot X holds _____ cups of water less than Pot Z.

EXERCISE 52

1. Work with your friends.
   You need a 1-liter beaker.
   Get a container which
   can hold 1 liter of water.
   Pour 1 liter of water into the container.
   Then mark the water level and write 1 ℓ on the
   container.

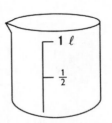

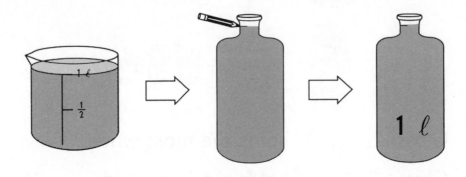

2. Get a bucket and a basin.
   Estimate the amount of water
   each container can hold.
   Then check by measuring with the 1-ℓ container you
   have made in Activity 1.

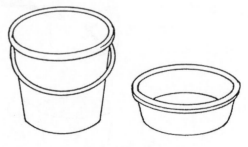

	My estimate	My measure
The bucket	about _____ ℓ	about _____ ℓ
The basin	about _____ ℓ	about _____ ℓ

EXERCISE 53

1. Fill in the blanks.

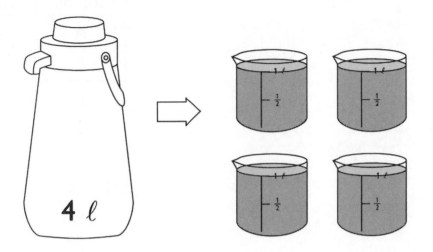

(a) The flask can hold _____ liters of water.

(b) The capacity of the flask is _____ liters.

2.

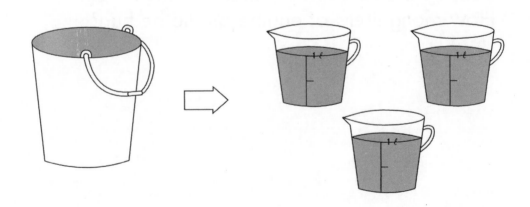

(a) The bucket can hold _____ liters of water.

(b) The capacity of the bucket is _____ liters.

3. This table shows the sale of gas at two stations. How much more gas did Station B sell than Station A?

Station	Gas sold
A	458 ℓ
B	600 ℓ

---

4. John bought 5 bottles of engine oil.
   Each bottle contained 4 liters of engine oil.
   How many liters of engine oil did he buy?

EXERCISE 54

1. The capacity of a tank is 250 gal.
   It contains 105 gal of water.
   How many more gallons of water are needed to fill up
   the tank?

---

2. Lauren poured 16 qt of orange juice equally into 8 jugs.
   How many quarts of orange juice were there in
   each jug?

3.

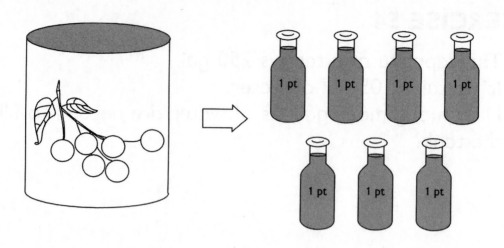

(a) The container can hold _____ pt of water.

(b) The capacity of the container is _____ pt.

4.

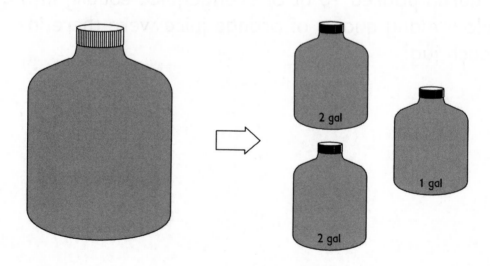

(a) The container can hold _____ gal of water.

(b) The capacity of the container is _____ gal.

EXERCISE 55

1. A group of children made this picture graph to show the colors they like best.

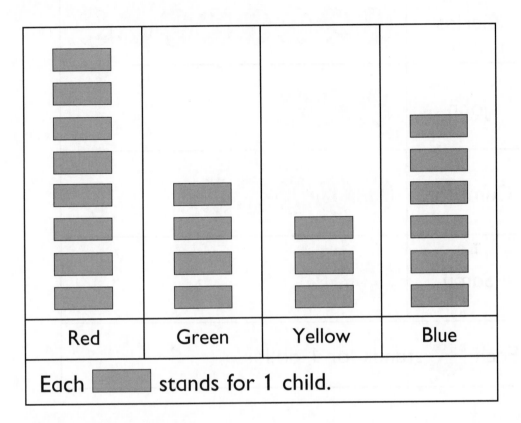

Study the graph.
Then fill in the blanks.

(a) _____ children like yellow best.

(b) _____ children like blue best.

(c) _____ more children like blue better than green.

(d) _____ is the most popular color.

(e) _____ is the least popular color.

2. This picture graph shows the amounts of money four boys have.

Carlos	⚪⚪⚪⚪⚪⚪⚪⚪
John	⚪⚪⚪
Cameron	⚪⚪⚪⚪⚪
Samy	⚪⚪
Each ⚪ stands for 1 dollar.	

Study the graph.
Then fill in the blanks.

(a) Carlos has _____ dollars.

(b) Cameron has _____ dollars.

(c) Carlos has _____ dollars more than John.

(d) Samy has _____ dollars less than Cameron.

(e) _____ has 3 dollars less than Carlos.

EXERCISE 56

1. Joe made this picture graph to show the number of different types of toys he has.

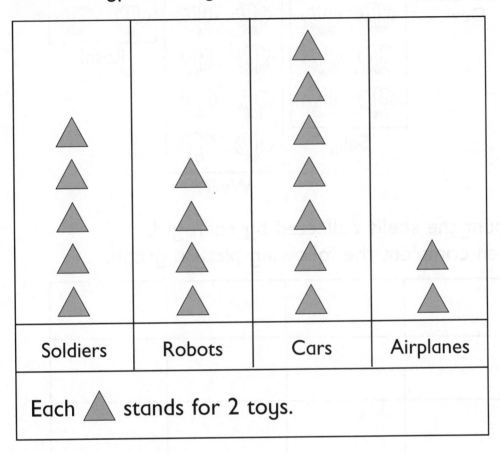

| Soldiers | Robots | Cars | Airplanes |

Each ▲ stands for 2 toys.

Study the graph.
Then fill in the blanks.

(a) Joe has _____ soldiers.

(b) He has _____ cars.

(c) He has _____ airplanes.

(d) He has _____ more cars than robots.

(e) He has _____ fewer airplanes than soldiers.

2.

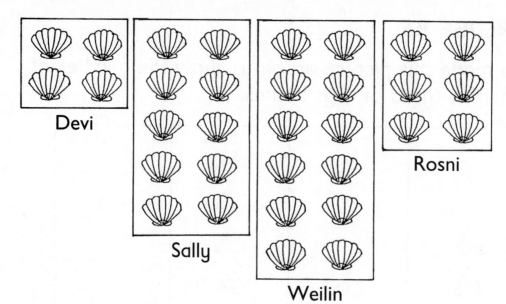

Devi

Sally

Weilin

Rosni

Count the shells collected by each girl.
Then complete the following picture graph.

⬤			
⬤			
Devi	Sally	Weilin	Rosni
Each ⬤ stands for 2 shells.			

EXERCISE 57

1. Fill in the blanks.

(a) Each ★ stands for 5 fish.

★ ★ stand for _____ fish.

(b) Each ◆ stands for 10 cars.

◆ ◆ ◆ stand for _____ cars.

(c) Each ● stands for 4 people.

● ● ● stand for _____ people.

2. (a) Each ■ stands for 3 balloons.
    Color the correct number of squares to show
    15 balloons.

    □ □ □ □ □ □ □ □ □ □

(b) Each ▲ stands for 10 flowers.
    Color the correct number of triangles to show
    60 flowers.

    △ △ △ △ △ △ △ △ △ △

3. This picture graph shows David's savings in four months.

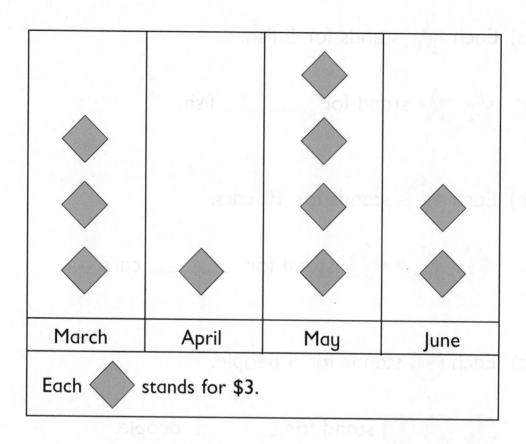

| March | April | May | June |

Each ◆ stands for $3.

Study the graph.
Then fill in the blanks.

(a) David saved _____ in March.

(b) He saved $6 in _____.

(c) He saved the most in _____.

(d) He saved _____ more in May than in April.

(e) His total savings in the 4 months is _____.

EXERCISE 58

1. This bar graph shows the number of stamps collected by four children.

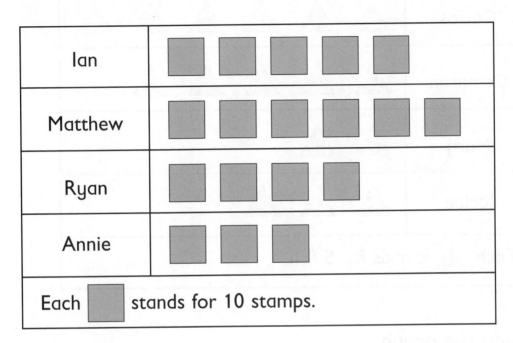

Study the graph.
Then fill in the blanks.

(a) Ian collected _____ stamps.

(b) _____ collected the greatest number of stamps.

(c) _____ collected 30 stamps.

(d) Ian collected _____ more stamps than Ryan.

(e) Annie collected _____ fewer stamps than Matthew.

(f) Ryan and Annie collected _____ stamps altogether.

2. This picture graph shows the number of fish caught by four children.

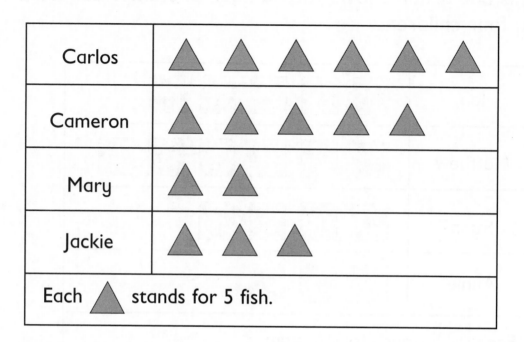

Carlos	▲ ▲ ▲ ▲ ▲ ▲
Cameron	▲ ▲ ▲ ▲ ▲
Mary	▲ ▲
Jackie	▲ ▲ ▲

Each ▲ stands for 5 fish.

Study the graph.
Write YES or NO for each of the following:

(a) Carlos caught 6 fish.	
(b) Jackie caught 15 fish.	
(c) Cameron caught 2 more fish than Jackie.	
(d) Mary caught 20 fewer fish than Carlos.	
(e) If Carlos caught 2 more fish, he would have 20 fish.	

EXERCISE 59

1. Join each pair of objects that have the same shape.

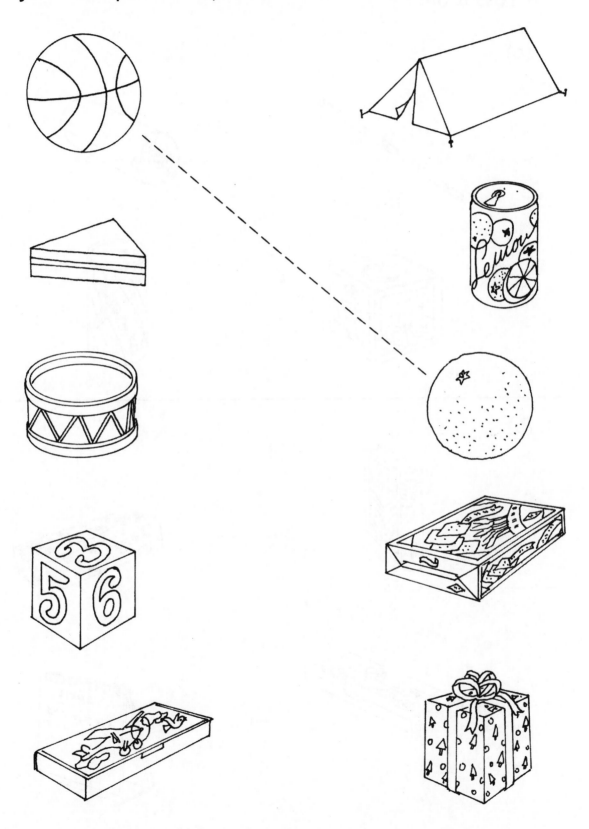

2. Which object does not have the same shape as the others?
Cross it out.

(a)

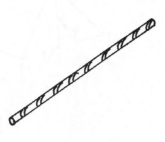

(b)

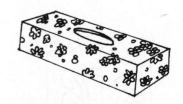

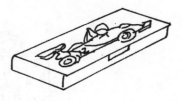

3. Name the shape of the face which is shaded.

(a)

_____

(b)

_____

(c)

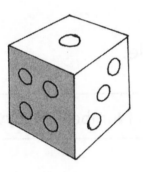

_____

(d)

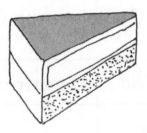

_____

(e)

_____

(f)

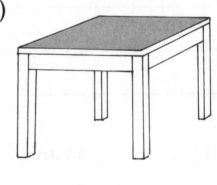

_____

4. Count the flat faces and curved faces of each solid.

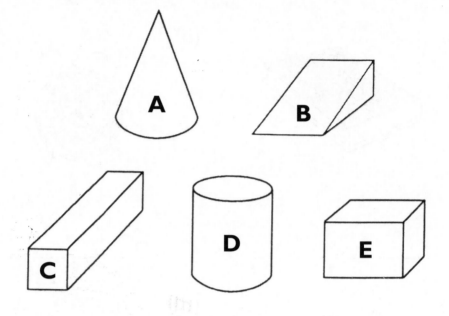

(a) Complete the following table.

Solid	Number of flat faces	Number of curved faces
A		
B		
C		
D		
E		

(b) _____ faces of Solid B are triangles.

(c) _____ faces of Solid C are squares.

(d) _____ faces of Solid D are circles.

EXERCISE 60

1. Join the two parts that form a circle.

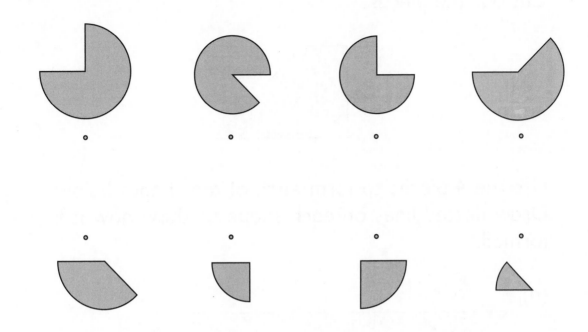

2. Join the two parts that form a square.

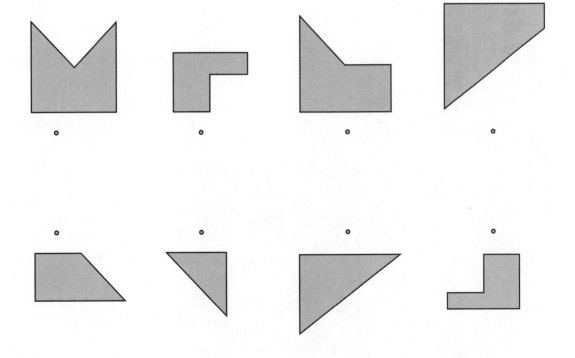

143

EXERCISE 61

1. Trace this shape 4 times on a piece of paper.
    Cut out the pieces.

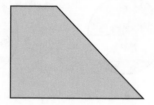

Use the 4 pieces to form each of the shapes below.
Draw dotted lines on each shape to show how it is
formed.

(a)

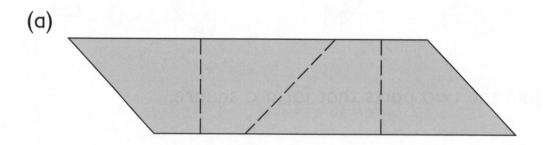

(b)

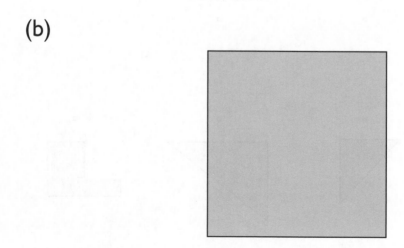

(c)

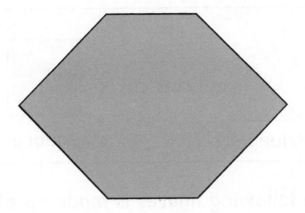

(d)

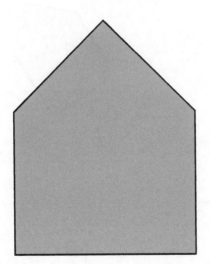

EXERCISE 62

1.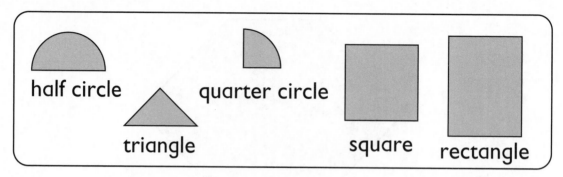

half circle   quarter circle   square   rectangle   triangle

Each of the following figures is made up of two of the above pieces.

Draw a dotted line on each figure to show how it is formed.

Name the two pieces.

(a)

half circle

_____

_____

(b)

_____

_____

(c)

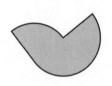

_____

_____

(d)

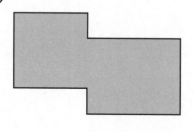

_____

_____

(e)

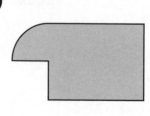

_____

_____

2. Draw dotted lines on each figure to show how it is formed by the given shapes.

(a) 2 rectangles:

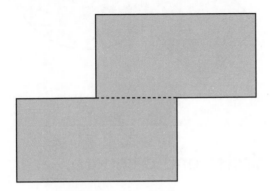

(b) 1 rectangle and 2 squares:

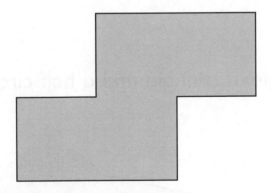

(c) A half circle and a rectangle:

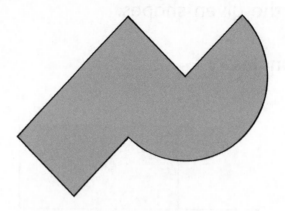

(d) 2 quarter circles and a square:

(e) A rectangle, a triangle and a half circle:

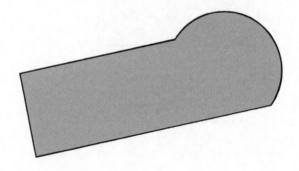

EXERCISE 63

1. This figure is formed by two straight lines and two curves.

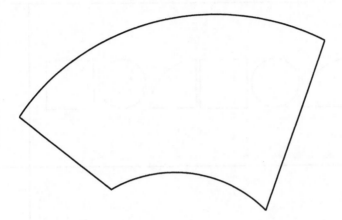

   Draw another figure with two straight lines and two curves.

EXERCISE 64

1. Study each pattern.
   Then color the shape that comes next.

(a)

(b)

(c)

(d)

2. Study each pattern.
   Then draw the shape that comes next.

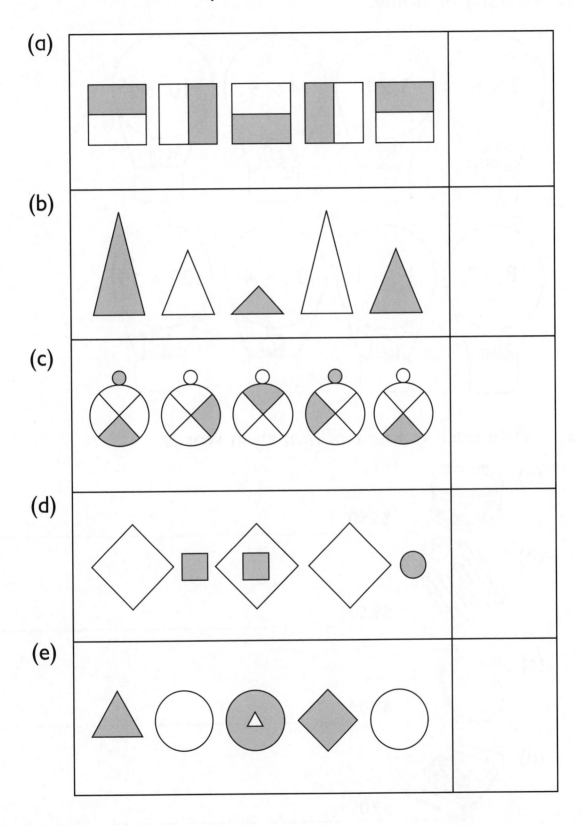

(a)

(b)

(c)

(d)

(e)

REVIEW 6

1. Multiply or divide.

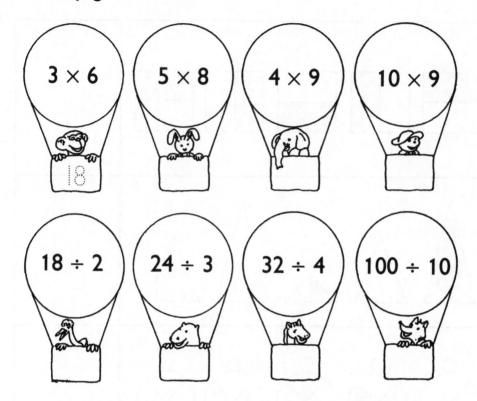

2. Write each amount of money in words.

(a) $5.90 _____

(b) $9.50 _____

(c) $5.09 _____

(d)  $9.05 _____

3. Color each circle to show the given fraction.

$\frac{5}{6}$　　　　$\frac{3}{4}$　　　　$\frac{2}{3}$

Then write the fractions in order, beginning with the smallest.

_____

4.

(a) The solid has _____ flat faces.

(b) _____ faces are rectangles.

5. (a) Mr. Ward has 40 chickens.
   He draws this diagram to show the number of chickens he has.

   Each △ stands for _____ chickens.

(b) Melissa draws this diagram to show the number of books she has read.

   Each ◯ stands for 5 books.

   Melissa has read _____ books.

6. David has **8** quarters and **12** dimes.
   How much money does he have altogether?

---

7. Juanita bought a key chain for **$3.95**.
   She gave the cashier **$10**.
   How much change did she receive?

---

8. Juan paid **$35** for **5** concert tickets.
   How much did **1** concert ticket cost?

9. Matthew read 210 pages of a book in two days.
   He read 145 pages on the first day.
   How many pages did he read on the second day?

10. Andy saves $4 a week.
    How much can he save in 6 weeks?

11. John saved $245.
    He saved $65 less than his sister.
    How much did his sister save?

EXERCISE 65

1. Color the pair of shapes that have the same size.

(a)

(b)

(c)

(d)

(e)

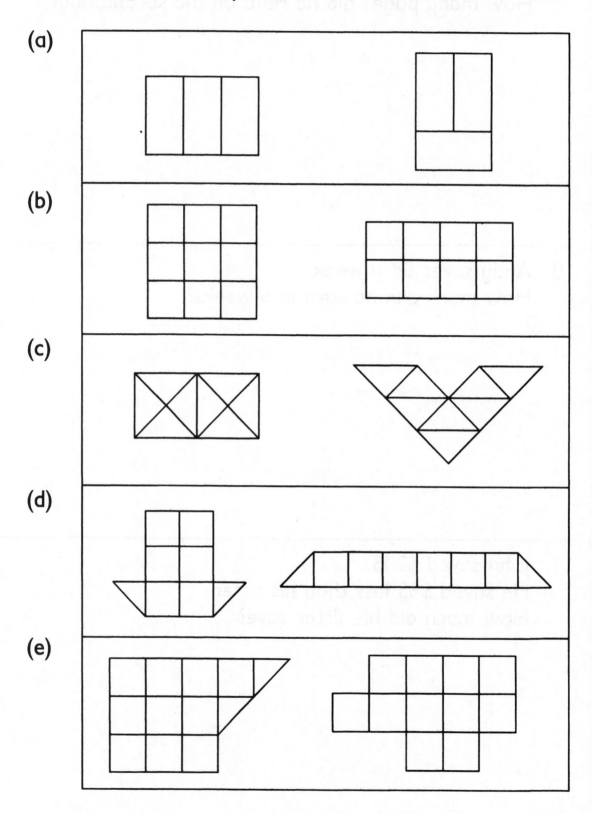

156

2. Circle the bigger shape.

(a)

(b)

(c)

(d)

(e)

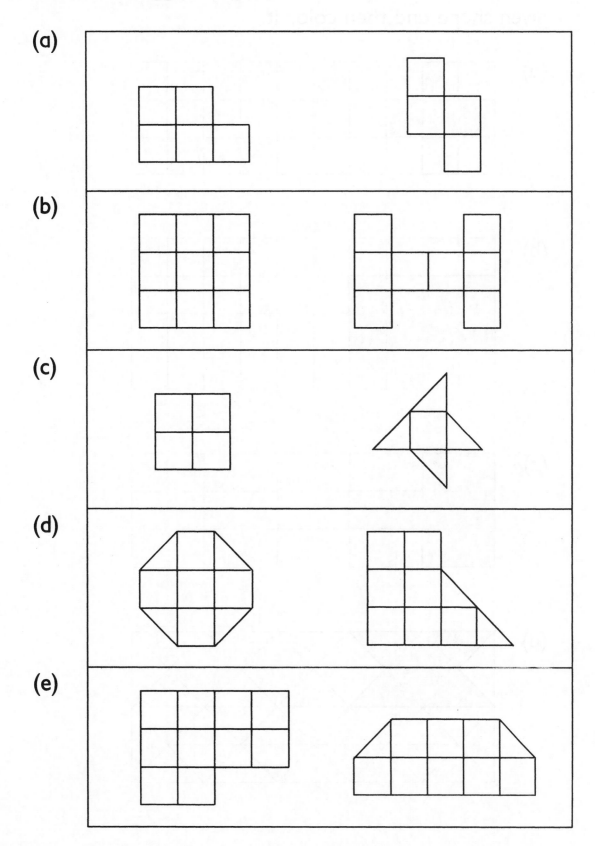

157

3. Draw another shape which has the same area as the given shape and then color it.

(a)

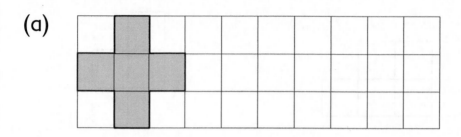

(b)

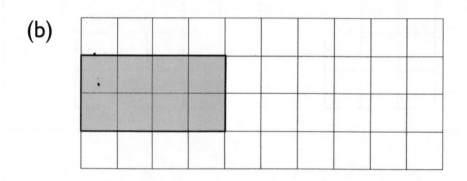

(c)

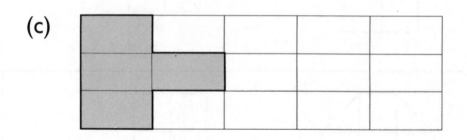

(d)

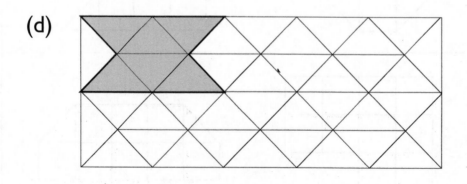

EXERCISE 66

1. Join the two shapes that have the same area.

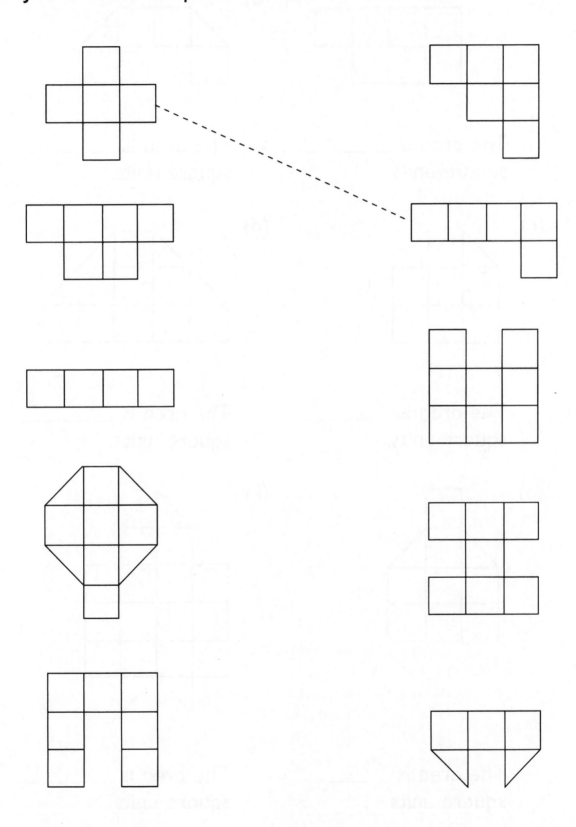

2. What is the area of each shape?

(a)

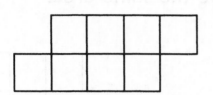

The area is _____
square units.

(b)

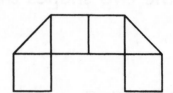

The area is _____
square units.

(c)

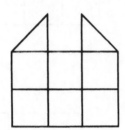

The area is _____
square units.

(d)

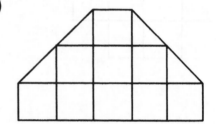

The area is _____
square units.

(e)

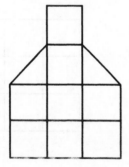

The area is _____
square units.

(f)

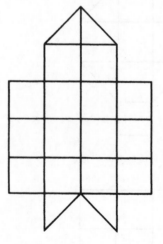

The area is _____
square units.

EXERCISE 67

1. Draw another shape which has the same area as the given shape and then color it.

(a)

(b)

(c)

(d)

(e)

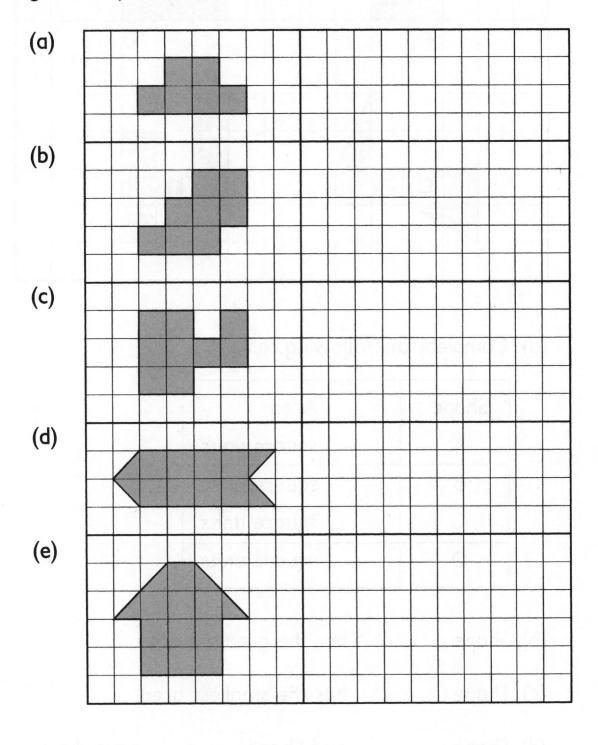

2.

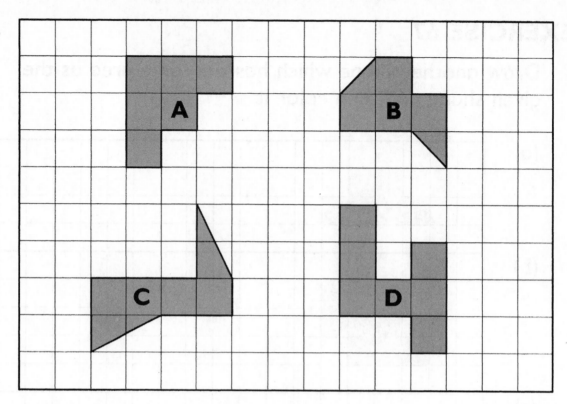

(a) Complete the following table.

Shape	Area
A	_____ square units
B	_____ square units
C	_____ square units
D	_____ square units

(b) Shape _____ has the greatest area.

(c) Shape _____ has the smallest area.

(d) Shape _____ and Shape _____ have the same area.

REVIEW 7

1. What number does each set of number discs stand for?

(a)

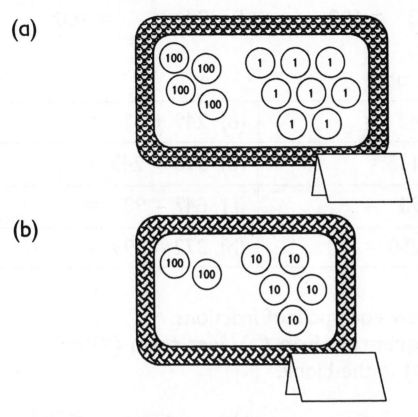

(b)

2. Fill in the missing numbers.

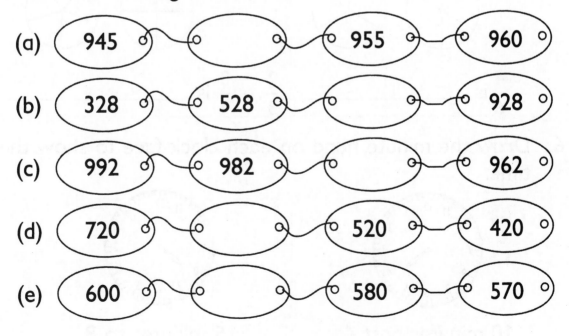

(a) 945 | | 955 | 960

(b) 328 | 528 | | 928

(c) 992 | 982 | | 962

(d) 720 | | 520 | 420

(e) 600 | | 580 | 570

3. Fill in the missing numbers.

    (a) $100 - \boxed{} = 41$ (b) $100 - 58 = \boxed{}$

    (c) $\boxed{} + 63 = 100$ (d) $24 + \boxed{} = 100$

4. Add or subtract.

(a) 108 + 42 =	(b) 249 + 51 =
(c) 365 + 135 =	(d) 598 + 243 =
(e) 486 − 90 =	(f) 647 − 98 =
(g) 875 − 250 =	(h) 372 − 299 =

5. Color to show each pair of fractions.
   Then write **greater than (>), less than (<)** or
   equal to (=) in the blank.

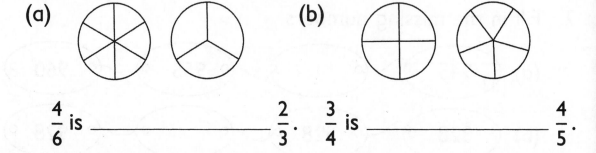

   (a) $\dfrac{4}{6}$ is _____ $\dfrac{2}{3}$.   (b) $\dfrac{3}{4}$ is _____ $\dfrac{4}{5}$.

6. Draw the minute hand on each clock face to show the
   time.

   10 minutes past 4   15 minutes to 8

7. Arrange these figures into the three groups given below.

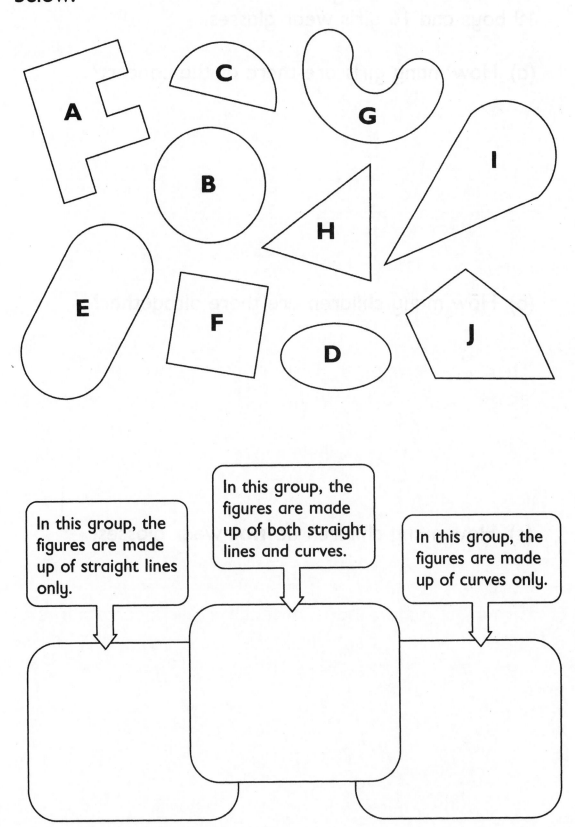

In this group, the figures are made up of straight lines only.

In this group, the figures are made up of both straight lines and curves.

In this group, the figures are made up of curves only.

8. There are 120 boys at a concert.
   There are 85 more girls than boys.
   19 boys and 16 girls wear glasses.

   (a) How many girls are there at the concert?

   (b) How many children are there altogether?

   (c) How many children do **not** wear glasses?

9. Rolando scored 89 points in English, 91 points in Science and 90 points in Mathematics.
   Find his total score in the three subjects.

---

10. John, David and Peter share 24 picture cards equally.
    How many picture cards does each boy get?

---

11. Mrs. Smith bought 9 pieces of rope.
    Each piece was 5 m long.
    How many meters of rope did she buy altogether?

12. Kelly has $6.80.
    She wants to buy a stamp album that costs $8.50.
    How much more money does she need?

---

13. Pablo's family drinks 6 qt of milk a week.
    How many quarts of milk do they drink in 10 weeks?

---

14. Sara made 32 muffins.
    She put them into boxes of 4 each.
    How many boxes of muffins did she have?

REVIEW 8

1. Write the missing numbers.

    (a) 2, 4, 6, ____, ____, ____, ____, ____, ____, ____

    (b) 3, 6, 9, ____, ____, ____, ____, ____, ____, ____

    (c) 4, 8, 12, ____, ____, ____, ____, ____, ____, ____

    (d) 5, 10, 15, ____, ____, ____, ____, ____, ____, ____

    (e) 10, 20, 30, ____, ____, ____, ____, ____, ____, ____

2. Fill in the blanks with the correct units.

| m | cm | kg | g | ℓ | h | min |

    (a) Morgan drinks about 2 _____ of water a day.

    (b) Jake takes about 5 _____ to brush his teeth.

    (c) Sara bought a piece of ribbon 2 _____ long.

    (d) Lindsey bought 600 _____ of grapes from a market.

    (e) Ryan paid $25 for 2 _____ of ground coffee.

    (f) Tyrone's shop opens 10 _____ every day.

    (g) The height of a table is 72 _____ .

    (h) The capacity of a can is 5 _____ .

3. Color each shape to show the given fraction.

(a)

$$\frac{2}{3}$$

(b)

$$\frac{3}{4}$$

(c)

$$\frac{3}{8}$$

4.

A   B

(a) The area of Shape A is _____ square units.

(b) The area of Shape B is _____ square units.

(c) Shape _____ is bigger than Shape _____.

5. Each of the following figures is made up of two shapes. Draw a dotted line on each figure to show how it is formed and name the two shapes.

(a)

The figure is made up of a

_____ and a _____.

(b)

The figure is made up of a

_____ and a _____.

170

6. Arrange the numbers in order, beginning with the smallest.

(a)

_____

(b)

_____

7. Fill in the blanks.

(a)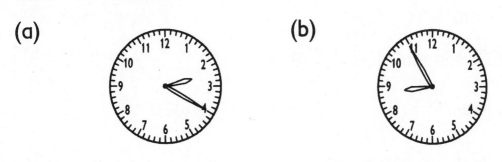

(b)

The time is _____ minutes past 2.

The time is _____ minutes to 9.

(c)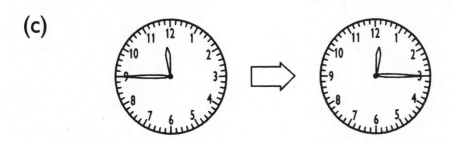

There are _____ minutes from 11:45 a.m. to 12:15 p.m.

8. Jen made 240 cupcakes.
   She made 405 muffins.
   How many more muffins than cupcakes did she make?

_____

9. 10 dolls cost $70.
   Find the cost of 1 doll.

_____

10. Mike bought 20 apples at 4 for $1.
    How much did he pay?

11. Wendy made 153 cookies.
    89 of them were chocolate cookies.
    The rest were sugar cookies.
    How many sugar cookies did she make?

12. Samantha saved $10.40.
    She saved $3.95 more than her sister.
    How much did her sister save?

13. A tank can hold 8 buckets of water.
    The capacity of the bucket is 4 liters.
    What is the capacity of the tank?

14. Warner bought a radio for $6.90 and a toy robot for $8.20.
    How much cheaper was the radio than the toy robot?

---

15. The capacity of a tank is 50 gal.
    It contains 38 gal of water.
    How many more gallons of water are needed to fill up the tank?

---

16. Juan paid $5.20 for a pen and a notebook.
    The pen cost $1.80.
    What was the cost of the notebook?

17. Five bags of sugar weigh 40 lb.
How much does 1 bag of sugar weigh?

1 bag of sugar weighs _____ lb.

18. A tank contains 17 gal of water.
25 more gallons of water are needed to fill it.
What is the capacity of the tank?

The capacity of the tank is _____ gal.

19. A magazine costs $3.80.
A book costs 2 quarters more than the magazine.
Find the cost of the book.

The book costs _____ .

20. A toy costs $6.05.
    Ryan has 24 quarters and two nickels.
    Does he have enough money to buy the toy?

_____

21. Andy bought an eraser for 29 cents.
    He gave the cashier 2 quarters.
    How much change did he receive?

    He received _____ cents.

_____

22. Bonita has 32 quarters, 12 dimes, 6 nickels and 3 pennies.
    How much money does she have?

    Bonita has $_____.